THE COURSE

A Novel by
Dennis Torres

Publisher: Dennis Torres

Hardback ISBN: 978-0-9980824-2-4

Paperback ISBN: 978-0-9980824-4-8

Contact Dennis Torres dennistorresmalibu@gmail.com

To my beautiful wife and muse Averi, my parents Ruth and Joseph Torres, my maternal grandparents Jacob and Celia Adler and my literary agent Bertha Klausner all of whom encouraged me to embrace life to the fullest and share my journey through writing.

To my spiritual teacher Eknath Easwaran for his pragmatic wisdom and guidance.

And to my many students who have inspired me with their quest to live a meaningful life. Being their professor has been an honor and a blessing.

Other Novels by Dennis Torres
The Amazon of Ray Goldberg Rivera
There Are No Good Giants
Far From The Ocean

As long as we see life divided into good and bad, right and wrong, success and defeat, birth and death, as long as we groan under the tyranny of likes and dislikes always seeking the pleasant and avoiding the unpleasant, so long will our mind be like a sea that is agitated all the time.

Eknath Easwaran

PREFACE

Of the three courses Professor Santiago Meyer taught in the MBA program at Grand Reflection University (GRU), a mid-sized college located in La Verdad, Arizona, his Course entitled *Acquiring Wealth, Power, Success, Morally and Ethically (AWPSME)* was the most popular.

He developed the Course at the request of the Dean who decided the Program curriculum needed a class on ethics. Never having taught the subject, Professor Meyer reached out to colleagues who taught it at other universities across the Country and asked for their guidance. While they generously shared their syllabuses along with the text books they used, none of these resonated with him. So he researched the subject on his own and discovered a foundational belief among many scholars that by the time a student reaches the graduate school level they have long established their values of right and wrong and little could be gained by parroting any such values in class. Moreover, that morals and ethics differed dependent on a student's culture. Professor Meyer had observed this very notion in the Ethics exercise GRU mandated for each incoming cohort of MBA students wherein the students were separated into teams with each team given an ethics problem to solve. The consensus solution was then presented by the team leaders in front of a panel of faculty members. One of the problems queried what the students would do if they saw a fellow student cheating on an exam. Going in, the students knew that University policy required they report any instances of cheating to their professor. Consequently the students knew what the panel of faculty members wanted them to say and they dutifully obliged. Another question dealt with the issue of plagiarism and again the students dutifully recounted GRU's policy on that issue too, stating that plagiarism was an ethical breach. Over the years of observing this exercise Professor Meyer discovered when he provided his students with a safe environment virtually all of them revealed they would not report a policy offender; while they were fiercely competitive they did not come to school to be enforcers for the faculty. Furthermore, many of the students were foreign nationals who came from cultures where their ethics differed from GRU's on these very issues. For example, competiveness in their cultures to gain access to higher education was so extreme that grades were all that mattered and the means to attain those grades justified the end. Additionally, in some of these cultures, plagiarism was considered acceptable as in "why reinvent the wheel" and therefore not a breach of ethics. When Professor Meyer presented these findings to the faculty he argued that requiring students to be untruthful was counterproductive to the educational process and should be eliminated. But the faculty was unwilling to make changes primarily because

GRU's Christian culture required strict adherence to its established cannons that held such breaches were unacceptable and wrong.

Not wishing to dictate a singular standard of ethics that would do little to enhance a student's educational experience Professor Meyer set about developing an ethics curriculum that would instead challenge the students to think critically about the subject and decide for themselves the path they wanted to follow. He knew too, that the title of the Course had to be provocative enough to attract students, because new courses were not listed in the Catalog until they had gained a sustainable following; they typically attracted only three to five students for the first year or two until word got out that the Course was either worth taking or not in which case it would be added to the school's Catalog as a regular class or dropped all together. He believed that simply calling the class something like *Ethics* would not attract many students so he entitled it, *Acquiring Wealth, Power, Success, Morally and ethically* incorporating topics of interest to the typical MBA student.

Acquiring Wealth, Power, Success, Morally and Ethically (AWPSME)

Syllabus

CLASS ONE

INTRODUCTION

Thoughts on Beliefs
Moral and Ethical Concerns

Professor Meyer: "Welcome to Class one on Acquiring Wealth, Power, Success, Morally and Ethically or if you prefer AWPSME. During our time together I want you to know that just because I am your professor you do not have to agree with me. The purpose of this Course is not for me to feed you information to be regurgitated back on an exam, but to provoke thought and in the process encourage you to think critically and come to your own conclusions, not just about the subject matter of this Course, but most everything throughout your lifetime. To accomplish this it is my intention to provide you with a safe environment so that you feel free to explore and question that which is being said by me, your fellow students and anything you might read in the Course text books so you can express your own thoughts and opinions without concern for judgement. In this regard I ask each of you to be open minded and neither give offense, nor take offense in presenting or reacting to anything being presented.

I am aware many of you have been acculturated to view academia through the lens of grades with getting an 'A' as not only the primary goal, but the only goal. In my opinion academia should do away with grades altogether they are both a flawed measurement and divertive, if not counter, to the process of education. That said I am required to grade so here's my philosophy and criterion on that process. I see my role as a provider of a service and you as the customer paying me to provide you with that service. As such if you never come to class or do any assignments that's up to you. But since I am required to grade I will do so as follows. If you actively participate in class and put a conscientious effort into both the classroom discussions and your assignments you will get a good grade. But if someone puts in a greater effort that person will get a better grade."

Student: "Professor, will you let us know throughout the semester how we rank in terms of getting an A and if necessary what we will have to do to get one?"

Professor Meyer: "I unfortunately anticipated that question so here's my answer. Yes, but the responsibility to inquire is on those of you who want to know. Are there any other questions?"

Hearing none he continued.

Professor Meyer: "To get the most from this Course it is important that you to be an active participant. To facilitate this, unlike in your other classes, you will not be able to use your laptops or hand held computers during class unless I specifically ask you to look up something on the Web."

Student: "Professor, how will we be able to take notes?"

Professor Meyer: "You are free to take handwritten notes during class and general notes for each class will be posted on the Course Website. Additionally, when you leave class each day you are encouraged to keep a journal of what was covered during the class along with your thoughts on the discussions. These will be useful in completing your weekly assignments and the Reflection Paper due at the end of the Course that will serve as your final examination. Are there any questions?"

Hearing none he continued.

Professor Meyer: "Now I would like for each of you to stand up one at a time beginning with the row to my right and briefly introduce yourself starting with your name followed by where you are from, what you hope to get out of this Course and what you want to do with your life going forward."

Of the twenty nine students, approximately half were foreign nationals mostly from China, India, Japan, Saudi Arabia, Kuwait, Philippines, Switzerland, France, Germany and Nigeria. Of those with finance concentrations, most stated their goal was to work on Wall Street in brokerage, M&A, investments or for a hedge fund and acquire enough wealth to retire within five to ten years. Of those with marketing concentrations the majority aspired to go into non-product specific branding with the same stated goal of building wealth quickly and retiring young. Of those with other concentrations some were interested in creating an App for the purpose of gaining wealth quickly and retiring young. Only a few expressed interest in dedicating themselves to improving the lives of others and the environment with acquiring money being secondary or not of any great concern. These revelations did not come as a surprise to Professor Meyer as he had experienced similar declarations from past cohorts. He sensed they were the result of a generation raised on entitlement although he did not hold that against them. He understood if this was so, they were a product of their development over which they had little control. As one former student explained, "I know my parents started with nothing, worked hard and sacrificed a lot to get what they have. But I was raised differently. They started me at the level they had finally attained and that's my bottom. It's not my fault that I only want go up from there."

While previous generations were raised on an ethic of hard work and sacrifice, many of his students' generation were raised where the delineation between wants and needs was more often than not

*unclear and both of these were often provided without effort or sac-
rifice on the student's part. The latest clothes, car, computer, cell
phones, vacations, sports lessons, music lessons, even college and
grad school, were provided at little or no cost to them and they were
raised knowing nothing else. Their parent's ethic of hard work and
self-sacrifice so their children would have it better than they did,
produced a generation raised on unintended entitlement, lacking
the same drive, patience and willingness to labor for the fruits it
might produce. In a way they reminded Professor Meyer of the story
of Siddhartha prior to his becoming the Buddha, who was born
and raised within the walls of his father the King's palace and thus
had no awareness of the world outside where poverty, pain, sick-
ness and death existed until one day on a rare outing he accidently
caught a glimpse of these things and the shock of it sent him on a
journey to discover the meaning of life. It was Professor Meyer's
goal that this Course would inspire the students to take a similar
journey of discovery.*

Following the introductions Professor Meyer continued.

Professor Meyer: "Thank you for your introductions. Now
that we know each other a little better I would like to explore what the words wealth, power, success, morally and
ethically mean to you and how I intend to use them in this
Course. Let's begin with the word wealth. What does wealth
mean to you?"

Student: "To me wealth means having a lot of money."

Professor Meyer: "What is a lot of money to you?"

Student: "Enough that I can buy whatever I want and do whatever I want without worry."

Professor Meyer, "So how much money is that?"

Student: "At least ten million dollars!"

Professor Meyer: "That certainly is a lot of money, but will it be enough to satisfy you in the long run with the cost of houses, cars, clothes and travel all raising with inflation? Somebody else, how much money will it take to make you feel wealthy?"

Student: "I would be satisfied with a million dollars."

Student: "I think I will need a minimum of two million invested wisely to live really well."

Student: "I think it will take at least five million."

Student: "To be really wealthy I think in today's dollars you will need something north of twenty to fifty million."

Professor Meyer: "Some years ago I saw a TV program where a reporter stopped people in the street and asked them a similar question: 'How much more income would you have to have in order to feel financially comfortable?' From those persons earning minimum wage, to those who were middle class, and those who were high income earners, they all answered between ten to twenty percent more than they were presently making. What does this tell you?"

Student: "That people always want more!"

Student: "That most people will never be satisfied."

Professor Meyer: "Yes, so it seems, that we in American society are conditioned to want more irrespective of how much we have. By way of example, on the eve of each New Year there's a cultural tradition of making resolutions for the year ahead. Last year on TV I saw a street reporter asking people what their resolutions were and a man who identified himself as a hedge fund manager, told the reporter that he had made a billion dollars in the current year and his resolution for the New Year was to double that. To me it was very telling of how our society has conditioned us to always want more and to never to be satisfied.

If you look up the word wealth on the Internet there are several definitions such as, '*the abundance of valuable possessions or money; plentiful supplies of a particular resource; an accumulation of valuable economic resources that can be measured in terms of either real goods or monetary value. In western countries net worth is the most common measure of wealth and it is determined by taking the total market value of all physical and intangible assets owned, then subtracting all debts. Wealth can be categorized into three principal classes: personal property, including homes or automobiles; monetary savings; and the capital wealth of income producing assets, including real estate, stocks, bonds, and businesses. It is the abundance of valuable financial assets or physical possessions which can be converted into a form that can be used for transactions.'*

For the purpose of this Course however, I would like to focus in part on a measure of wealth used by the authors of *The Millionaire Next Door,* which is one of the text books I chose for this Course. And that measure is, 'if your income ceased today, how long you could maintain your current lifestyle.' I believe the authors' stated that the typical real millionaire could maintain their current lifestyle somewhere between twelve and sixteen years without earning new income. I like this measure because many high income, high lifestyle persons who are looked upon as wealthy could not maintain their lifestyle for more than a few months should their income cease. We'll cover this in greater depth in our Class on Wealth. Are there any questions so far?"

Hearing none he continued.

Professor Meyer: "Now let's discuss Power. What does power mean to you?"

Student: "I looked it up when I decided to take this class. According to the dictionary it is *the ability to direct or influence the behavior of others or the course of events.*"

Professor Meyer: "Thank you. That is a common definition, but I'm looking for what it means to you personally."

Student: "That I don't have to listen to anybody; I can be my own boss and do whatever I want."

Professor Meyer: "Yes, that's more in line with how I see power being used in this Course; not so much the ability to influence or control others, but the capacity to make your own choses in life, such as the type of work you want to do or whether you want to work at all. Again we will get into this more in depth in the Class on Power. Now for the word Success. What does success mean to you?"

Student: "Accomplishing what I set out to do."

Student: "Making a lot of money."

Student: "Winning more than losing."

Student: "Having enough money."

Student: "Living the good life."

Student: "Being recognized by my peers and society as having accomplished something worthwhile."

Professor Meyer: "Yes all those things are good measurements of success, but the definition I would like to concentrate on in this Course is the experience of feeling fulfilled."

Student: "Professor what do you mean by fulfilled?"

Professor Meyer: "An experiential state of joy; of being full; of lacking nothing; of being blessed. I use the word experiential rather than feeling, because feeling is typically associated with thought and physical sensations. We will get more into this definition in the Class on Success.

Now for the meanings of morally and ethically. What is your understanding of morals and ethics and the differences between them?"

Student: "From what I read, morals relate to individual behavior whereas ethics relate to the behavior dictated by a culture."

Professor Meyer: "A good dictionary definition thank you."

Student: "Morals deal with issues of right and wrong as defined by certain organizations like a religion or society such as lying, cheating, stealing, pre-marital and extra marital sex, plural marriage and homosexuality, whereas ethics are issues of right and wrong defined by the community and society as applied to business, medicine and law."

Professor Meyer: "Another good dictionary definition. For the purpose of this Course however, I would like us to explore the idea that morals and ethics are not universal absolutes, but subject to cultural and societal differences. And that the morals and ethics of one culture or society may be totally opposite those of others, yet still be considered moral and ethical.

Student: "Maybe for some things, but not for others."

Professor Meyer: "Can you elaborate on that and give us an example of what you mean."

Student: "Murder is universally wrong."

Professor Meyer: "Well this may challenge you, but I suspect that in a metaphysical sense right and wrong don't really exist, even when it comes to murder, meaning actions and consequences are just actions and consequences, it is we who categorize and judge them."

Student: "How can you say that?"

Professor Meyer: "As a soldier the U.S. Government sent me to Vietnam to kill people and told me it was the right thing to do."

Student: "But that was war and you were killing our Country's enemies."

Professor Meyer: "Murder is often defined as the unlawful killing of a human being with premediated malice and that was certainly the government's intent and that of many soldiers. While it was considered lawful to our Government it was certainly considered unlawful to the Vietnamese being killed. To them I was the bad guy; after all they didn't come here to kill me and my family! As I explained earlier you don't have to agree with me. I just want you to think critically about what is being said.

Let me use another example to provoke some thought on this issue of right and wrong. We in the U.S. love our dogs, some of us even more than our children, yet in some cultures they slaughterer and eat puppies and dogs like we do to chickens and other animals. Is killing puppies and dogs for food right or wrong?"

Student: "I think it's horrible. Puppies and dogs are sweet innocent creatures and the thought of anyone killing and eating them is repulsive and morally wrong."

Professor Meyer: "Some of your fellow students who are Hindu's might think eating meat from cows like those McDonald's hamburgers is horrible, repulsive and morally wrong as cows are sacred in their culture."

Student: "Professor, I'm from Switzerland and it's a dirty little secret that some Swiss eat dogs too."

Professor Meyer: "Thank you, I never heard that before, but it is certainly relevant to the point I am trying to make because the Swiss are considered part of Western culture when it comes to cultural morals and ethics. So let's examine how we come by our beliefs in general.

There's a story about a pot roast that may help shed some light on this question. It goes like this. A newlywed girl was preparing a pot roast dinner for her husband and her visiting parents. When she put the uncooked pot roast into the pan her mother told her she had to first cut a little bit off of each end before cooking. When the girl inquired why, her mother told her because that is the way it's done; that's the way her mother taught her to do it. Subsequently, when girl saw her grandmother she asked her the same question and received the same answer; that's the way her mother taught her to do it. And when the girl inquired of her great grandmother why she cut the ends off the pot roast before cooking, her great grandmother thought about it for a few moments trying to recall the reason, then answered 'because the pot roast was always larger than the pan I had back then.' The point of the story is that many things we do are done without questioning them, because that's the way they have always been done or that's the way we were taught to do them.

Here's another story to further illustrate this. I like to explore the California deserts. In one of them, the Anza Borrego State Park, there are a few places where you can still see wagon tracks made in the eighteen hundreds as part of the westward migration. Besides the thrill of seeing history firsthand they remind me of why train tracks are the width they are. Does anyone know or want to take a guess why train tracks are the width they are?"

Student: "Because that's how the first train cars were built?"

Student: "They're engineered for optimum efficiency as in speed versus drag?"

Professor Meyer: "How about this: The standard railroad track gauge in the U.S is four feet, eight and a half inches wide; an odd number to say the least. It is widely held that this width was derived from the tracks built in England where they are said to be based on the width of an imperial Roman war chariot (Rome having once occupied England), which were in turn designed to accommodate the width of the horse's rear that pulled the chariot."

Following laughter from the students.

Professor Meyer: "Again, the point I am trying to make is that more often than not we just accept things rather than question them. That is, we don't think about what we believe or why we believe what we do. Who can tell me what critical thinking means?"

Student: "To examine something in the process of understanding it?"

Student: "To analyze data."

Professor Meyer: "Yes, both of those definitions are correct. Here's another from the many online definitions: 'Critical thinking is the intellectually disciplined process of actively and skillfully conceptualizing, applying, analyzing, synthesizing, and/or evaluating information gathered from, or generated by, observation, experience, reflection, reasoning, or communication, as a guide to belief and action.'
    I'll add to this by offering, before you can think critically you will have to set aside all preconceptions. Some may argue that this is impossible or nearly impossible and perhaps it is, but I will enhance the discussion by drawing a parallel

to my experience as a professional mediator and arbitrator of litigated cases; a profession where the principle of neutrality is so paramount that practitioners are often referred to as 'neutrals.' Prior to a mediation when I would read the briefs sent to me by lawyers from each side, I would often form an opinion as to which party had the better argument or which party was wronged from the standpoint of equity or which party had the better case under the law. But once the mediation or arbitration session began I was so driven by my obligation to be neutral along with an innate curiosity to discover the positions as understood by each side, I felt as neural as a human being could be. In other words, I set aside my preconceptions and was so neural I could argue both sides with the same conviction, commitment and passion. This level of neutrality is what I would like you to consider as we explore the topics in this Course. For the purpose of critical thinking, instead of assigning your conditioned values of what is right and what is wrong I would like you to consider that those concepts are neutral and are only differentiated by the consequences associated with each of them and those consequences are neither good nor bad, but simply in the mode of Newton's third law which holds for every action, there is a reaction. In practical application, this means when you chose an action you also chose its reaction or consequence and there's no judgement involved.

One more thing, we are going to explore thinking critically about two kinds of knowledge, intellectual knowledge which deals with the faculty used to navigate our physical environment such as our day to day interaction with the phenomenal world, and spiritual knowledge which is the experiential state of unity that transcends thought. Both govern our choices, but I will ask you to consider the veracity in the saying '*your belief determines your action and your action determines your results.*' Are there any questions?"

Hearing none Professor Meyer continues.

Professor Meyer: "To begin this process I would like each of you to participate in an exercise I call *six degrees of separation* from the movie of the same title that posits everyone is somehow connected to one another through others they know by at most, six rounds of introductions. In this exercise however we'll explore our connections through mutual experiences. To begin, find a fellow student whom you do not know, or do not know very well, and take a minute to jot down your thoughts and impressions of that person, then take six minutes, three minutes for each of you, to discover at least five things you have in common such as you both have sisters with the same name or you both lived in Turkey or you both collect stamps, anything you have in common and write them down so you can share them with the class when you are finished. Be prepared to be surprised. In previous classes some students discovered they were dating the same person and in others that they were related, but did not know this beforehand."

Following the exercise.

Professor Meyer: "Okay, who's ready to tell us what they discovered?"

Student: "We both have been to Tasmania. We both come from a large family; he has twelve brothers and sisters I have ten. We both are into martial arts. Our favorite food is Italian. We both like traveling and hiking. And we both subscribe to Travel magazines.

Professor Meyer: "Were you surprised?"

Student: "Yes, very much. After all how many people have been to Tasmania and come from such large families today."

Professor Meyer: "Thank you. Who's next?"

Student: "Like in your other class we found out we are distant cousins yet have never met. And we're both left handed and have birthdays in the same month, January. We both are risk takers; I've done sky diving and he races motorcycles. We both are creative writers, me poetry and he short stories. And we both like beer better than wine."

Professor Meyer: "Excellent! Who's next?"

Student: "Both our fathers are named Alex. We both like sushi. We both have been to every State including Alaska and Hawaii. Her boyfriend was in the Peace Corp and I have a cousin who was in the Peace Corp. We both had dogs growing up. And we both went to Catholic school."

Professor Meyer: "Excellent! Let's hear one more before moving on."

Student: "We're both socially conscious and both have volunteered at non-profits; me with The Boys and Girls Club and he with Habitat for Humanity. We both grew up in the mid-west, Ohio for me and Minnesota for him. We both are fourth generation Germans. We both like to bowl. And we got so wrapped up in talking about other things we ran out of time before coming up with anything more."

Following laughter from the students.

Professor Meyer: "Thank you for that. Now having done this exercise, how many of you now feel differently about the person you spoke with than you did beforehand?"

All hands go up.

Professor Meyer: "How many of you feel closer? More connected?"

All hands go up.

Professor Meyer: "The point of the exercise is to help you experience the unity of your sameness rather than the separateness of your differences and the meaning of that insightful quote from Irish poet William Yeats, 'a stranger is a friend you haven't met yet.'

Moving on, to set the stage for what is to come in the Course, I want you to consider why you believe what you believe and hold on to those beliefs as universal truths expecting that others will accept them the same as you do. Also, that much of what you believe is acculturated and based on unverified information gained or acquired from others rather than part of your own direct, firsthand objective knowledge. That is, as the saying goes, 'you see the world not as it is, but as you are.'

How many of you have heard of the Danish fairy tale called the Ugly Duckling?"

Several hands go up.

Professor Meyer: It's about a duckling that did not look like the other ducklings and therefor was considered ugly; this made the ugly duckling very sad. At the end of the story the ugly duckling saw a reflection of beautiful white birds flying overhead that looked just like it did and discovered it was not an ugly duckling after all, but a beautiful swan and it was very happy.

To me in a macro sense, the point of that story is how our acculturation can lead us to believe anything different is an ugly duckling whether the difference is one of religion, language, appearance, occupation, gender etc. In Vietnam I was surprised to hear more than one soldier say of the Vietnamese, 'these people are stupid they can't even speak English.' It never occurred to those soldiers, that to the Vietnamese they were the ugly ducklings. Once I inadvertently stopped in a bar in Venice, California only to discover it was a lesbian bar and immediately realized I was the ugly duckling not the women I saw. The same happened when I was visiting the Island of Jamaica where the dominate population is black. How many Americans visiting England for the first time comment that the English drive on the wrong side of the road and have a funny accent rather than consider perhaps we drive on the wrong side of the road and we have a funny accent? Some of us are acculturated to think that gay, lesbian and transsexual people are ugly ducklings. Yet science tells us they are as normal as everybody else. When I was growing up, there was a popular soup call alphabet soup. Besides broth and vegetables it contained tiny pieces of pasta in the shape of alphabet letters. When a spoon was dipped into the soup there was no telling what letters would be on it when it was brought back out. It's the same with creating a human being, we never know what combination of X and Y chromosomes are going to be in the primordial soup that makes us who we are. While our acculturation may tell us that a straight male and straight female are normal, science tells us there are actually many more genders that are just as normal although maybe not as common. It might surprise some of you to know that all fetal genitalia are the same, all are phenotypically female, that is to say we all had female genitalia at one time and could have gone either way or even ended up with both. You could have been a boy name Sue, a girl named Sam or a person named Jose Maria or Maria Jose; no offense to my Spanish friends.

After the students laugh, Professor Meyer continues.

Professor Meyer: "What I am trying to say is, for the most part our world is our mind. Virtually everything we know of life and the world around us passes through that mind. It is the Grand Central Terminal for all our senses. We do not hear with our ears, nor see with our eyes, nor taste with our mouth nor touch with our hands, those anatomical parts are merely sensors that send a signal to our brain which filters the signals through our collective experience to determine how to respond. That is why some of us love chocolate others do not, yet chocolate is neither good nor bad it's just chocolate.

From the moment we are born our brain gathers information about the world from our unique experiences. From that perspective our world is uniquely unlike the world of others. Everything we experience has its influence on how we interpret life. While anthropologists and psychologists may argue that the basis of how we see the world and how we respond to it is mostly formed during our first five years of life, it does not stop there, our interpretation of that world is continuously taking place throughout our lifetime.

Much of how we see the world comes from our early experiences with our parents, neighbors, family and friends. When we are born our mind is somewhat empty of cognitive experience and like a sponge it soaks up all sensory input, trying to make sense of it. With little life experience to go on much of this sensory experience is confusing and in an effort to make sense of it we interpret it a little differently than others, but in general accept it as truth. If we are told that the tooth fairy gives us money for our fallen teeth and Santa Clause is responsible for all those fun gifts at Christmas this becomes our universal truth. Early in our life when we watched movies and television it is likely we believed much of what we saw on the screen was real. So when we saw Superman we believed he could fly and had ex-ray vision. And when we saw Michael Jackson we believed he was 'The King of Pop.' And that Bruce Springsteen was 'The Boss.' Or if we lived Atlanta that Coke was far better than Pepsi. Or if we were from New York that the Yankees were far better than The Cardinals and that the people who lived in the North were better than the people who lived in the South and vice versa. And if we were from Chicago we likely believed it made the best pizza in the world. Or if we liked fashion magazines that skinny girls were hot and fat girls were not. These early experiences and beliefs tend to stay with us throughout our lives so that many years later when we go to a movie we fall in love with Brad Pitt or Jennifer Aniston or Tom Cruise or Julia Roberts because we just know by looking at them and hearing their voices that they are such wonderful people and we believe every good thing that is written about them, and defend them against those who believe otherwise. And we spend our hard earned money even when we don't have it to spare, by buying things they endorse like the Lancom Julia Roberts uses and the Under Armour clothes that The Rock promotes, and Old Navy because of Kristen Bell, not caring if they cost more than others. We go to plastic surgeons and have our noises made to look like Paris Hilton's or breasts like Pamela Andersen's. We go to the gym to have abs like Matthew McConaughey and if Shaq says drink this or Kobe says eat that we don't question it. We believe we know them yet we don't. We believe red wine is far superior to white wine because others say so; or that imported wines, cheese, chocolates etc. are

better than domestic ones even if they aren't. We believe
that monogamous marriage is better than plural marriage,
or different sex marriage is better than same sex marriage
or that working with your brain is better than working with
your hands or the opposite depending on who you hang
with. Or that sex workers are to be valued less than those
who trade in just about anything else.

When I was in the military and living in North Dakota
where the winter temperatures with wind chill often got to
forty and fifty below zero and there were few trees or mountains or lakes, I was shocked when I met a man and his wife
in a tiny isolated town who told me they had just moved
back there after years of living in Acapulco, Mexico and
did so because they missed the beauty of their hometown.
Having been to sunny, tropical Acapulco I could not understand why anyone would give it up for the biting cold and
isolation of the North Dakota plains. But they obviously saw
the world differently than I did.

I also found it difficult to watch my good German friend
eat one pickled pigs foot after another or my Japanese friend
eat the raw parts of just about anything. Did you chose your
religion or was it given to you? When your parents said you
were a particular religion and everyone who wasn't would
not get into Heaven you likely believed them with every fiber of your being. And when something terrible happened
to someone who was not of the same religion it was because
god punished them. And when the same thing happened
to those who were, it was simply gods will.

Perhaps your parents told you not to smoke, that it was
bad for you, yet they smoked. Or your minister proclaimed

'judge not least ye be judged' and he or she was judgmental. Or you were told by family and friends that Republicans are good and Democrats are bad yet you encountered people you respected who held a different view. All these things and more influence how you see life.

Next I would like you to think about the meaning of life in general. Where we came from and where we go when we die. In exploring this let's consider two philosophical points of view. One, that there is no purpose to life, that is to say no meaning or order; a sort of a nihilist view that there is no god, no heaven or hell, no universal law, so we might as well do whatever we want because it doesn't matter in the grand scheme of things. And the other, that there is indeed meaning to life even if we don't know what that is. An order that some people refer to as natural law or metaphysical law or god's law or simply a unity like 'the butterfly effect' where every thought, utterance and action affects everything else. There are variations on these ideas, but for the purpose at hand let's consider these two ideas as a base. And again, I remind you, you are free to disagree with anything I say. Just raise your hand and I will give you the opportunity to express your point of view or simply challenge the one being expressed.

To continue, according to commonly accepted history the greatest scientific minds in the world once had no doubt what-so-ever that the earth was flat and traveling across it would likely result in falling off the edge. I recall reading that this belief was so sacrosanct that scientists who held different views where considered mentally deficient and sometimes put to death. Over the years many beliefs once accepted as absolute truths have been debunked and discredited. Once there were only five senses, now it's accepted there are nine including thermoception, the sense of temperature; equilibrioception, the sense of balance; proprioception the sense of spacial orientation; and interoception, the sense of one's physiological condition. Another, that humans evolved from Apes. Now some believe that humans did not evolve from apes, but just share a common ancestor that lived millions of years ago. Some have argued, perhaps in jest, if we evolved from apes how come there are still apes? In any event, it is likely that many of today's absolute certainties will be set aside sometime in the future as flawed or untrue like that belief in the Tooth Fairy and Santa Clause. How many of you once had no doubt of their existence.

Many hands went up.

Professor Meyer: "The same could be said for many of our beliefs as adults such as, that in war god is on our side; that child labor is pure evil; that homosexuality is an abomination; that marriage between races should not be permitted; that abortion is murder etc. By a show of hands, how many of you have ever felt you were so right you would bet a million dollars you were right, or you would bet your life or your mother's life that you were right, only to later discover you were wrong?"

Every hand goes up.

Professor Meyer: "My guess is that it wasn't a onetime occur-rence either. It's likely we all had the experience more than once of being absolutely certain we were right, only to find out we were wrong. Given this, how can we ever feel cer-tain about anything? We can't! The point of this is that our life experience would work best if we condition ourselves to think critically and consider other possibilities along with their inherent consequences rather than believe in abso-lute certainty. Life is a process which means when new ideas come to mind they influence the process. And to consider too, that our beliefs are the result of our unique cultural conditioning and experiences to the extent that two truths can be one hundred and eighty degrees in opposition yet both be valid. Once when I was in high school, I got a traffic ticket for making a U turn on a bridge. It was a draw bridge that was opening to let a boat pass underneath and I didn't want to wait so I made a U turn. And when I went to court to fight the ticket there was a case being heard ahead of mine involving a man who got a ticket for going through a red light. When the man's lawyer cross examined the police of-ficer who issued the ticket, he asked the officer, 'Where were you when you observed my client allegedly going through a red light?' And when the police officer indicated he was on the opposite side of the traffic signal the man's lawyer said, 'Then you did not see the same light my client saw' meaning the police officer saw the light from his perspective on the opposite side of the intersection. To my surprise the judge dismissed the case. Now we are all likely conditioned to as-sume that the light on a traffic signal is the same color on both sides of the intersection at the same time and we are very likely correct. But in the case at hand the lawyer made a valid point that perspective can change so called facts, and what is observed is observer subjective which is another way of saying we don't see things as they are, but as we are. There's even a theory in quantum physics called *the observer effect,* a phenomenon in which the act of observation alters the behavior of the particles being observed.

Now consider when it comes to your beliefs, if you had been adopted as an infant into a family that had entirely different beliefs, such as religious beliefs, than the ones you were raised in, do you think you would still have the same beliefs you have today."

Student: "It's a little hard to assimilate that thought, but intellectually the answer has to be no."

Student: "Yes, I believe I would have eventually found my path back to Jesus regardless of what my adopted family's religion was."

Professor Meyer: "Perhaps, but on what basis do you feel that would be the case? If you were raised in Saudi Arabia by Muslim parents like your classmate sitting across from you, or Hindu or Sikh parents like your classmates from India, don't you think you would likely have had a very different perspective on Christianity. "

Student: "Professor I understand what you mean, it's just hard for me to separate my entire life identify and imagine what you are saying."

Professor Meyer: "That's the challenge of critical thinking. It challenges us to open our minds to consider even the most radical of thoughts and ideas. Keep in mind this discussion has nothing to do with religion, or getting you to change your mind, but exploring why we believe what we believe and how those beliefs influence our life experience. One of Albert Einstein's most famous quotes is, 'we cannot solve problems with the same thinking we used when we created them.' In B school we refer to this as 'thinking out of the box.'"

A couple of real life stories come to mind that might further illustrate this idea of how acculturation and conditioning affects our thinking. One of them is about identical twin sisters born in Mexico. Because they were adopted out as infants to two different New York families each one grew up without knowing about the other. But through fate they were reunited when a mutual acquaintance couldn't help but notice their similar appearance. One twin was attending Hofstra University and the other Adelphi University. They had a lot of similarities besides their looks such as, both of their adopted fathers had passed away from cancer, both liked to dance, both had similar gestures, similar voices, similar habits and similar interests, but one was raised Jewish and the other Roman Catholic and these faiths were a strong, integral part of their individual identity. You can read about them in their book entitled 'Identical Strangers.'

The other story is about a man named David Good who was born in the Amazon rainforest to an indigenous Amazonian tribal woman and an American Anglo father who was an anthropological researcher from the

University of Pennsylvania in Philadelphia. When his father returned to the University he brought infant David with him. Growing up in America David used to tell his friends that his mother had died in a car crash because he did not want them to know 'my mom's a naked jungle woman eating tarantulas.' His mother was born and raised in a remote jungle village that still had no plumbing, electricity, written language, markets, currency or medicine as we know it. Her age was unknown, because her tribe, the Yanomami only count up to two, anything beyond that is simply called 'many.' You can imagine the different perspectives on life David would have had if he had been raised in the Yanomami culture. How this story came to be was his father had spent so much time with the tribe during his research that as a single man the tribe's leader offered David's mother to him as was their custom; she was only nine to twelve years old at the time and his father was thirty six. David's father saw no problem with this because he was living there and this was their culture. Not being obsessed with numbers, the tribal custom betrothed girls even before birth to tribesmen for later consummation. While girls had a right to refuse, in David's case, his mother had feelings for his father. As to ageism, it was the cultural age that was important to them. When this story came to light some in America accused David's father of having sex with an underage girl, but he assured them that she was at the age of consent, at the time. Of course there was no way to prove it either way because her culture didn't count age above two. Besides how this illustrates the affect of cultural conditioning on our beliefs, I have another question for you to consider, does one culture have the right to dictate to another culture what is right or wrong for them?"

Student: "Professor I understand the point you are making, but I'm still having a hard time accepting that a nine to twelve year old girl should be having sexual relations with a thirty six year old man."

Professor Meyer: "So are you saying that the tribal culture is somehow less valid than the culture you were brought up in?"

Student: "I don't think a girl of that age is physically or mentally mature enough to have sex much less give informed consent."

Professor Meyer: "As to your point about physically maturity, remember she gave birth to a perfectly normal baby. Wouldn't that indicate she was biologically mature enough to have sex? But the question at hand is not about biology or sex, it's about one culture having the moral authority to dictate right and wrong to another culture?"

Student: "I think in some circumstances yes."

Professor Meyer: "What circumstances would that be?"

Student: "Maybe if their culture was into cannibalism and they were killing and eating humans."

Professor Meyer: "Sounds like a slippery slope to me, remember in our western culture while we don't usually eat human flesh we've been killing humans since the beginning of our existence and continue to do so to this present day notwithstanding there have been reputed instances of cannibalism in western history, most notably about the Donner Party."

Student: "I see your point, but somehow our killing seems more justifiable than a bunch of primitives raiding villages, chopping off heads and eating their enemies."

Professor Meyer: "That's exactly the point I am trying to make. We tend to believe that our culture is somehow superior to that of others, which in my way of thinking seems subjective and arrogant. And since you broached the subject of age of consent regarding sexual relations, what does that mean?"

Student: "The minimum age at which an individual is considered legally old enough to consent to having sex."

Professor Meyer: "Do you know what that age is in Arizona?"

Student: "I think it's eighteen."

Professor Meyer: "Yes. What do you think the age of consent is in the Philippines?"

Student: "Probably fifteen."

Professor Meyer: "Let's hear from our Philippine student."

Student: "It's twelve."

After audible gasps from some students.

Student: "I'm not defending this, but to the undereducated poor villagers there are reasons it makes sense."

Student: "The idea that a twelve year old girl can consent to have sex or that somebody would even want to have sex with a twelve year old girl is crazy."

Professor Meyer: "How many of you agree with that statement?"

Most hands go up.

Professor Meyer: "Well apparently millions of people in the Philippines disagree with you. Perhaps because twelve is typically the age where a girls starts menstruating which is likely a sign that she is biologically ready to procreate. I'm not agreeing or disagreeing, just pointing out an example how cultural differences of right and wrong influence our morals and ethics. Now just to provoke more thought on this subject, what do you think the age of consent is in Nigeria?"

Student: "I don't know, but the fact you asked the question, my guess is that it's lower than that in the Philippines?"

Professor Meyer: "You are right, it's eleven. How about in the country of Yemen?"

Student: "I'm afraid to ask?"

Professor Meyer: "Officially there is no minimum age in Yemen, because the law requires that couples must be married before they can engage in sex. But unofficially the age is nine because many marriages take place between children of that age to forty or fifty year old men and guess what, they consider this moral and ethical. How many of you disagree with that stance?"

All hands go up.

Professor Meyer: "Then what should we do about it? Should we invade Yemen imprison all the men, rescue all the children and raise them right? Before you answer, consider this. What do you think the minimum age for boys and girls to legally have sex is in the United States?"

Student: "Didn't we already establish it's eighteen?"

Professor Meyer: "That is the legal age of consent in Arizona, in other States it's sixteen provided the age difference is not more than a couple of years, that protects many high schoolers, but neither of these is the age at which boys and girls can legally have sex."

Student: "What's the difference?"

Professor Meyer: "The age of consent refers to the minimum legal age an unmarried individual can give consent to have sex, but that age differs when that person is married. According to Internet research there seems to be no minimum age in some states in which a person can get married with parental or judicial consent and thus legally have sex."

Student: "I find that hard to believe."

Professor Meyer: "Natalie, why don't you Google that question and read out loud what you find."

After Googling the question.

Natalie: "Eighteen is the minimum marriage age in most states for a person to get married, but there are exceptions in every state that allow children younger than eighteen to marry, typically with parental consent or judicial approval. Nine states still allow pregnancy exceptions to the marriage age. In fact, twenty seven states do not specify an age below which a child cannot marry."

Professor Meyer: "Now scroll down and tell us what statistics show about marriage in some states."

Natalie: "Many of the states that provided data included categories such as fourteen and younger without specifying exactly how much younger some brides and grooms were. So while twelve year-old married children were found in Alaska, Louisiana and South Carolina, there may have been children younger than twelve wed in America between 2000 and 2010."

Professor Meyer: "Thank you. So do you still think the same way you did about the cultures in those countries that permit children to have sex and/or marry? Again, the purpose of this information is not to pass judgment, but to challenge our conditioned beliefs and motivate us to have an open mind and think critically. The end result does not have to dictate your opinion.

I'll illustrate this with another story. When I was studying for my master's degree at GRU's School of Law there was a sociology class discussion on a lifestyle concept called *The Family Bed* which was occasioned by a news article about a family who was practicing it and faced a good deal of negative criticism from the public. For those of you unfamiliar with *The Family Bed,* it is an age old concept in child rearing where children are welcome to sleep in the same bed with their parents even through their teen years to engender trust and bonding within the family dynamic. During our class discussion most of the class outwardly expressed their disgust with the parents who had permitted this and some likened it to pedophilia. And when I reminded them that it was very likely members of their own families did the same thing they turned on me in anger as if I were disrespecting them and their families. In explaining my remark I asked them to ponder the fact that it wasn't so long ago that most families lived in homes of less than six hundred square feet, like the primitive cabins on the prairie and those small tenement apartments in the cities that housed families of five to fifteen or more children all in one room sharing beds through adulthood. It was even common practice in those times for entire families to sleep together with visiting guests up until the nineteenth century when homes got larger and children had their own rooms. In fact when that happened many in society reacted with stinging criticism about how it could emotionally injure children to be separated from their parents. Thus, it was very likely their own grandparents and/or great grandparents and great, great grandparents practiced the family bed and they and their families turned out just fine. I was tempted to remind them that sleeping in one tiny room with a dozen or more kids didn't prevent parents from engaging in those acts necessary to produce more children, but given the emotionally charged environment in the classroom I thought better of it. While the point I made did not necessarily change any opinions it did temper some of the harshest criticism. It's just another example of conditioning versus critical thinking.

Now let's explore this issue a little more before we move on to the subject of judgment. How many of you are comfortable seeing a man and a woman kiss each other in a movie?

All hands go up.

Professor Meyer: "How many of you would be comfortable seeing a woman kiss another woman in a movie?"

A few hands go up.

Professor Meyer: "Now, how many of you would be comfortable seeing a man kiss another man in a movie?"

No hands go up.

Professor Meyer: "Now how many of you who have dogs or cats regularly kiss your dog or cat?"

Many hands go up.

Professor Meyer: "So it's perfectly acceptable for people to kiss an animal, but not for people to kiss another person of the same sex?"

Following laughter from the students.

Professor Meyer: "Why do you think that is?"

Student: "Because we are conditioned by our culture on what is acceptable and what is not acceptable?"

Professor Meyer: "Exactly. In other western cultures men kiss other men on the cheeks and both men and woman can go topless on the beach whereas those things are not acceptable here. Just two more examples of cutting the ends off a pot roast and something to think about.

One last story on this subject before we move on. As I tell the story I would like you to picture in your mind what I am saying and how you might have reacted.

When I arrived in Vietnam as a war time soldier, I and
likely most if not every American GI, was shocked to see
South Vietnamese soldiers in uniform walking down the
street holding hands like teenage lovers do in this Country.
Many American GIs took this to mean the South Vietnamese
soldiers were gay, because in their experience no hetero-
sexual man would ever think of doing such a thing especially not a soldier, especially not in uniform, and especially
not in a war and in public, and they did not want to serve
with them. In the Vietnamese culture however, men holding hands in public was simply an expression of bonding in
friendship. How many of you think you would have had a
similar reaction?"

Every hand goes up.

Professor Meyer: "This brings us to the topic of judgment.
GRU is a faith based Christian university that mandates undergraduate classes on the Bible. Even though they are not
required at the graduate level who can tell me what the
Bible says about judgment?

Student: "Judgement is mine sayeth the lord."

Student: "That judgment belongs only to God."

Student: "Judge not, lest you be judged."

Professor Meyer: "I see we have some Biblical scholars. Why
do you suppose the Bible says that?"

Student: "Because man is considered fallible and God isn't?"

Student: "Because mans' judgment is subjective and influenced by our conditioning so it's not to be trusted?"

Professor Meyer: "Those are good explanations. But why don't we practice this sage advice?

Student: "Because it's in our nature to be judgmental?"

Student: "Because society can't function without rules and rules inherently require some level of judgment?"

Professor Meyer: "I'm not so sure about judgment being a part of human nature per se rather than a conditioned trait. Whatever the case it seems that we as a society judge just about everything and everybody and do so as if our judgment is infallible. As to rules and rule enforcement, why couldn't we just have consequences without judgment? Why not look upon the purpose of rules and rule enforcement as simply being to protect society rather than to render judgment of the offender. Remember when I asked you if you have ever been absolutely certain about something only to find out you were mistaken? Think how much simpler, less stressful and more enjoyable life would be if you did not have to make judgments about others. Think about this statement. When you are certain you know what is right without accepting that you could be wrong you have sent innocent people to a life in prison and are responsible for irreparable damage and suffering in the world. Leave judgment to the universe or if you prefer god, and practice inalienable respect for all, which does not mean you have to agree with their actions. Again, I am not asking you to accept anything I say, only that you think critically about it.

Biblical advice further tells us 'As ye sow, so shall ye reap.' and 'Live by the sword, die by the sword' which derives from the Gospel of Matthew as follows, 'Then said Jesus unto him, Put up again thy sword into his place: for all they that take the sword shall perish with the sword.' I take this to mean there are inescapable consequences connected to our actions; those consequences are what the Buddhists' call Karma. Thus if we contribute to the suffering of others, we contribute to our own suffering and if we contribute to the welfare of others we contribute to our own welfare. If you deliberately do wrong to someone, the wrong will come back to you and if you are wronged by someone there is no need to retaliate because that person's karma, will retaliate for you. The underlying principal is that every action has within it an inescapable consequence. As such this frees us from having to redress a perceived wrong so we can go about our lives without that burden yet still learn from the experience. I have encountered many people in my practice as a mediator and arbitrator of litigated cases who were financially well off and otherwise in excellent health, but living in anguish because they were consumed by the need to retaliate against those they believed to have wronged them. This because they were conditioned by society to do so or risk being seen as weak and a loser."

Student: "You mean we should just turn the other cheek when someone does us wrong?"

Professor Meyer: "Isn't' that what Biblical wisdom tells us to do, 'to let go and let God', to go on with our life and let God or if you prefer the law of karma take care of the matter for us. Consider the alternative: engage in retaliation and be consumed by it. Granted there may be times when lawful action is warranted, but even then we should not let ourselves be emotionally or even intellectually consumed by retaliation. Think too, how many times we were misunderstood or were mistaken about another person's intention and actions. There's no point for you to retaliate if the process of retaliation is going to harm you. There's a wise saying 'anger is like taking poison and hoping the other person dies.' And another that reminds us 'we should be missionaries, not mercenaries.' I know this is difficult to assimilate since we been conditioned by society otherwise, but there are ways to resolve conflict without harming yourself or others. We will explore those more in class three entitled *Thoughts on Power*.

Now let's look further at where we get our beliefs by examining some of them. If I ask you, particularly those of you raised in this Country, who was the first president of the United States what would your answer be?"

Student: "George Washington."

Professor Meyer: "Does anyone dispute this?

No hands go up.

Professor Meyer: "Okay, Neal please Google 'who was the first president of the United States' and tell the class what you find."

Neal: "In November 1781, John Hanson became the first President of the United States in Congress Assembled under the Articles of Confederation which was our first constitution. George Washington was the first president under the present Constitution."

Professor Meyer: "How many others served as president of the United States after John Hanson and before George Washington?"

Neal: "There were thirteen other presidents"

Professor Meyer: "So technically George Washington was the fifteenth president of the United States and not the first and not only that, he wasn't elected by the citizens' at large, but by electors from each of the ten eligible states. Admittedly this is somewhat of a trick question, but it doesn't change the fact that the United States came into being under the Articles of Confederation which was the Country's first constitution and that there were fourteen presidents before George Washington. The point of this is to create an awareness that what we are taught to believe isn't necessarily true or entirely true and yet we are conditioned to accept it without questioning.

To further illustrate this point let's watch a short humorous clip from a video called '*Assume the Position*' produced by comedic actor Robert Wuhl and staged as a class lecture to real college students like yourselves, rumored to be at New York University."

Following the video.

Professor Meyer: "What message is Robert Wuhl trying to convey in the video?"

Student: "That history is presented to us as truth, but in reality may not be truth at all, but the product of those who write about history."

Professor Meyer: "Yes. There's an old saying that 'History is written by the victors.' It implies that history is not necessarily based on reality or facts, but the victor's interpretation of events. In a way it reminds me of the parlor game called *telephone* where a phrase is given to one person to pass on down the line to others and each time it's repeated it changes due to what the person thought he or she heard, so in the end, the last person hears a very different phrase.

Further to this point, when I was in Vietnam during the war it was well known that some of the television and newspaper reporters covering the war did not actually observe what they reported, but reported from the safety of their hotel rooms relying on stories told to them by others. And when those reports were broadcast and published they became facts."

Student: "That's like Robert Wuhl's quote from Tolstoy, 'History is a wonderful thing, if only it were true.'"

Student: "And his quote from the movie *The Man Who Shot Liberty Valance,* 'When the legend becomes fact, print the legend.'"

Professor Meyer: "What were some of the myths revealed in the clip that were taught as historical truths?"

Student: "That the midnight ride of Paul Revere to warn the colonists that the British were coming came from a poem written by the then popular poet Henry Wadsworth Longfellow called *Paul Revere's Ride.* That in reality, Paul Revere only rode some 12 miles and did not call out the British were coming. And that a postal rider named Israel Bissell actually rode some 345 miles to sound the warning."

Professor Meyer: "Yet we grew up being taught to believe that the fictional poem *Paul Revere's Ride* was in fact truth. If you go to Boston today the myth is still propagated as truth by the City to attract tourists in the same way Richmond, Virginia propagates the myth that Patrick Henry said "give me liberty or give me death" when in fact historians say that story came from a newspaper reporter who interviewed a person who claimed he was at the second Virginia Convention and paraphrased what he thought he heard."

Student: "Professor, I've been to Richmond and paid to watch the re-enactment at that Church where Patrick Henry supposedly uttered those words."

Professor Meyer: "Was that presentation of history as fact any different than watching a fictional movie based on actual events and believing it is all true?"

Several Students: "No."

Professor Meyer: "What other myths did Robert Wuhl speak to in his presentation?"

Student: "The story about Christopher Columbus going to King Ferdinand and Queen Isabela of Spain and asking them to finance his expedition to prove the world was not flat, but round."

Student: "According to Wuhl the origin of that story can be traced to author Washington Irving, a very popular writer who in the early 1800s wrote a fictional biography entitled 'A *History of the Life and Voyages of Christopher Columbus*'. His fictional story became a truth for many who read it and subsequently became a history that is still taught in schools today."

Professor Meyer: "Yes, and prior to viewing the clip, if I were to ask those of you from the United States who discovered America the answer would very likely be?"

Several Students: "Christopher Columbus"

Professor Meyer: "Yes and we even have a national holiday to celebrate the event each year. Aditi, please open your laptop and Google, did Christopher Columbus discover America and read out loud the citation you find."

Aditi: "Explorer Christopher Columbus (1451–1506) is known for his 1492 'discovery' of the New World of the Americas on board his ship the Santa Maria. In actual fact, Columbus did not discover North America. He never set foot in North America. During four separate trips that started with the one in 1492, Columbus landed on various Caribbean islands that are now the Bahamas as well as the island later called Hispaniola. He also explored the Central and South American coasts. We know now that Columbus was among the last explorers to reach the Americas, not the first. Five hundred years before Columbus, a daring band of Vikings led by Leif Eriksson set foot in North America and established a settlement."

Professor Meyer: Thank you. Just for fun here are a few more examples of how our beliefs have been acculturated.

The craving for beef was instilled in American culture during the 1950s; equating beef in particular steak, as high living; the spin off being hamburgers, deli meats etc. Prior to that beef was not a regular or desired everyday diet. This acculturated diet affected the entire eco system where rain forest was cleared to raise cattle and beef in particular steak, became equated to affluence and a superior way of life.

Here in the United States you can legally have the social equivalent of multiple wives or husbands by cohabiting in a plural arrangement with an unlimited number of women or men and it is perfectly legal as long as you are only married to one of them. And there is no limit to the number of children you can have. A recent news story about a religious group in Utah featured a man who had twenty seven 'wives' and three hundred children and it was all perfectly legal.

Among the Christian faithful it is generally conceptualized that the characters in the Bible really existed and that they were all European-like white and that Jesus was a white Christian and spoke English yet they were all from the Middle East likely spoke a dialect of Aramaic and Jesus was of the Jewish faith.

Whether or not Columbus discovered America or Paul Revere warned the British, or we believe steak equates to a superior way of life, or that plural marriage is good or bad, or Jesus and his followers if they existed were white and spoke English are not all that important. The point of this discussion is to create an awareness that our truths may not be everybody's truths or truths at all, but products of editorialized history and/or acculturation and conditioning. Of greater importance is, that the points raised inspire you to think critically instead of just accepting popular beliefs as absolute truths. After that, if you decide to maintain or accept the same beliefs at least it will be an informed decision rather than uninformed one.

Now I would like you to share your pre-class assignment on what you consider to be the most pressing moral and ethical issues challenging you today. Let's start on the right side of the room and go down each row and up the next time permitting."

Student: "Valuing money; I don't want my life to be ruled by money, but money is necessity to live in our society. Making ethical and moral sacrifices to survive workplace politics; while I'd rather always be genuine, sometimes even the best jobs require me to 'play the game.' Competing versus assisting; much of what I must do is based on competition. Competing for jobs against my peers or competing for network contacts; by nature I'd much rather assist my peers than compete against them. But is this the price of success. Success versus satisfaction; while I want to be successful in my career and in my life, I often struggle with the cost in terms of time, satisfaction, and happiness. Building a society based on debt instead of savings; our society encourages people to borrow money in order to start or continue their lives comfortably. Credit card debt; student loans; mortgages, car loans, small business loans, government loans, etc. Success at the price of the little guy; our economic system is built on the idea that someone always has to suffer. If there is a finite amount of available wealth and a certain percentage possesses most of it, some will have little to none of it. Being right versus acceptance or tolerance; in many situations, we act as if there is only one way to think, look, or act and if one does not abide by it, he or she is wrong. And the politics of saving face versus changing the way we think; in the U.S. we have a strong sense of history and constantly state that history repeats itself. History need not always repeat itself, but many decisions made in society are based upon popular habit versus doing what is right."

Professor Meyer: "Thank you. Next."

Student: "Whether or not I should be loyal to my employer when things are not going well? Should I be concerned about making money in my profession or personal challenge? When areas of my job are not being viewed how hard should I promote myself? Should I be concerned about the well-being of my company or just my profession? How much should we care about our environment? How are we caring for it now? When should a person give-back to society if they have the monetary capability to? Whether or not there should be laws passed that might infringe on people's rights? For example, are privacy laws to strict or not strict enough in society?"

Professor Meyer: "Thank you. Next."

Student: "Helping friends with tests/plagiarism. Telling little white lies that may not cause harm. Gossiping or telling other people stories/secrets. Remembering to treat others how I want to be treated. Maintaining my integrity and character when in a difficult situation in my personal life or at work. Abortion. Stem-cell research. Welfare/healthcare provided by the government for the poor. Research for genetic engineering. Business ethics: Disclosing all information and being honest and fair when handling other people's money. The war on terrorism. Capital punishment."

Professor Meyer: "Thank you. All very important. Next."

Student: "Money. Should I feel guilty for living a comfortable life while others in the world suffer? People family/friends. Who should I keep in my life and what should our relationship be? Society: What is my duty to those in my community? Charity: What is my duty to those who are not as fortunate as I am? How do I live a life of meaning and purpose? Job and career: What should I do with my life? Is working for a nonprofit a gallant decision? Or should I seek to contribute to society in some other way?

How much time should I dedicate to others? Is it okay to be a bit of a loner or should I try to connect more? Family duties: How should I treat blood relatives? Do I owe them a specific duty due to our biological relationship? If I adopt which I want to do later in life, how do I ensure that the child is treated equally to others? When and how do I tell them of their biological parents etc.? Interpersonal relations: What is my duty to those around me? Should I trust in others, or am I right to mistrust people? Should I always look for the good, give others the benefit of the doubt, turn the other cheek?

Good Samaritan: Am I wrong to turn a blind eye to people who I know are in trouble? When and why should I step in and intervene in situations? Am I polite enough to others, do I treat others with respect? Do I show them that I value them as humans or do I subconsciously or consciously treat them as less-important as myself? Politics and religion: How do I develop and maintain my positions while still respecting others? Do I have the right or the ability to judge others according to their beliefs? What makes me believe that my own personal views are correct and right for the world? Is there more than one right answer to a particular situation or is there indeed a single 'best' solution? Should I further seek to attach myself to a religion or am I fine as an agnostic? Sex and sexuality: Is it acceptable to have sexual relations before engagement? What are the social and personal constraints on my sexuality? Is it acceptable for me to dress and act the way that I do? Do I invite unwanted attention by my behavior, dress, actions or manners? Plagiarism: internet age: information is readily available – easier to take from others than create by oneself? Lying, mistrust, hypocrisy: Condemning others for living lives not unlike their own. Example "Thou shall not kill", but supporting abortion/death penalty. Respect for human life: wars, theft, murder, burglary, etc. Criminal affairs, death penalty, prison, justice systems, abortion, stem cell research etc. Sex and society: sex trafficking, prostitution, mutilation, purity honor killings. Sexual influence on children, either through media or through other means (religion/social norms); STDs, cheating, Divorce. Lack of commitment. Focus on immediate gratification, inability or unwillingness to think long term. People looking for quick fixes, want easy life without having to work for it. Valuing the family – raising children. Should people be allowed to have kids knowing that they will be unable to properly care for them? How should children be raised, carrot or the stick. Disappearance of cultures: Is the western world, American media, western religious beliefs, and customs dominating the world. Caring for and or respecting individuals other than oneself. Need to combat the 'me' generation. Money, wealth, power. Greed: focus on individual wealth, power, and success, what is the true measure of a man. Is it moral for leaders to live in wealth while their people suffer in poverty? What is the solution for third world nations, in particular what will become of Africa?

Western Media: Celebrity worship, reality TV. Filth, vulgarity, lack of respect for any type of moral or religious values. Politics/economics: Is communism inherently unjust/ evil/bad? What form of government works best? How does each society care for its people, especially the elderly, sick, less fortunate, etc. Is there really such a thing as a "just" war? Is the justice system indeed just/fair/equitable. Gender issues: What is the role of man/woman in society? Is it right for certain religions e.g. Islam to treat women as inferior to men? Is their treatment uplifting or degrading e.g. Sharia law. Animal cruelty: Is it acceptable to treat all animals as less than human? Is it okay to eat meat, but unacceptable to wear fur? If so, why? Can using animals for scientific experiments be justified if it saves the life of one or more humans? Should animals be kept in zoos? Should humans work to prevent species from going extinct? Environmentalism: What is man's duty to the world? Should he be allowed to use it as he likes or does he have a duty to preserve it and act on behalf of it? Is it socially responsible to drive big cars, use plastics, drink bottled water, etc.? Is there really such a thing as manmade global warming?"

Professor Meyer: "Thank you. All good questions and concerns. Next."

Student: "How do I find career success while doing
something that is fulfilling? How do I please my parents
while doing what I really feel is right for me? How do
I manage my work and social life in a way that doesn't
negatively affect either? How do I find and pursue the
occupation or industry that is exactly the place in my
life where I can be most effective. How do we preserve
the environment for our children without stunting economic growth? How do we build international unions
EU, MERCOSUR, without giving up to much control to
an entity? How do we provide a safety net for people in
society without taking away their incentive to work and
be entrepreneurial? How do we negotiate with rogue
states in a way that helps them demilitarize without an-
tagonizing them?"

Professor Meyer: "Thank you. Next."

Student: "The gray area between right and wrong what can
we technically get away with and what we know is right.
Difference between giving and helping others; our selfishness of helping ourselves. Happiness, it seems like so many
people are unhappy and can't take the steps to go in the
right direction. Trying to figure out what I want to do with
my life. I want to do something I love that helps people, I
just don't know what that is yet. Struggle with being successful versus something I love; I want to be able to do both.
Keeping straight on my moral compass. Keep to my beliefs
and not letting the world tell me otherwise. I don't want to
be selfish. I want to help others."

Professor Meyer: "Thank you. Next."

Student: "Limited financial resources are a problem affecting many students. The question is whether this constitutes a legitimization to circumvent copyright laws, trying to copy books, illegally download material etc. rather than prohibiting access. The possibility that I might be forced to engage in inhumane work practices in a later working environment e.g. firing employees, seeing persons as human resources with the only alternative to lose the job. Having to engage in environmentally harmful practices because a job requires it. Investing more time into career building and personal wealth than in helping others and focusing on leading a fulfilling life. In modern societies individual consumption of unneeded products tends to be valued more and associated more with the happy life than helping individuals in need and putting one's skills to good use. Often, short term comfort seems to be more important than environmental sustainability leading to gradual destruction of the environment. Personal enrichment and egoism often prevail over sharing and mutual benefit. Politicians frequently act against their own beliefs and long term benefits in favor of short term goals that can be effectively communicated through the media, but do not improve a problematic situation sufficiently."

Professor Meyer: "Thank you. All very good issues. Next."

Student: "Absence of Trust (i.e. government). Greed. Pride. Gluttony. Abortion. Capital Punishment. Human Cloning/ Stem Cell Research. Homosexuality."

Professor Meyer: "Thank you. Next."

Student: "Digital piracy (stealing) music, DVDs, and books. Consumption of Alcohol. Premarital sex.

Contributing to the destruction of the environment. Gambling. Ecological footprint/destruction of the environment. Abortion. Same sex marriage. Use of marijuana. Universal health care. Privacy vs. security."

Professor Meyer. "Thank you. Next."

Student: "Standing up for what you believe in. It is a personal challenge to me that I stand up for what I believe in, that I live my values in everyday life, privately as well as professionally and that I do not compromise my values to gain professional success, more money or even just to make an easy shortcut.

Doing the right thing. Doing the right thing because it is the right thing to do is something I strongly believe in and something that I feel challenged with often. I feel that in many situations I know what would be the right thing to do but that I also know alternatives that promise to be easier and potentially more successful. It is not always easy to follow through with the right thing and I can't say of myself that I have always succeeded in doing the right thing. Being an optimist. I consider my optimism and positive outlook on the world a great strength of mine and an important aspect of who I am. This kind of optimism is often challenged by the "real world" and I sometimes find it hard to maintain this optimistic view when the reality of the world seemingly proves me wrong. Specifically I find it hard to maintain this optimism when I see how many things go wrong in our world on a broad scope from international media and the narrow focus of a GRU classroom. I consider it a moral challenge to uphold my optimism despite how naïve others might consider this. Honesty. I personally feel challenged to maintain honesty in everything I do. This is especially so since often it is easy to identify easy ways out and it is hard to stick to the honest way of doing things. Additionally, I sometimes feel frustrated trying to be honest when I can see plenty of dishonesty in my surroundings and know that this might be the easier, less complicated, faster, less effort, option from time to time. Greed. Not only since the recent financial crisis came over us have I felt that our society is more and more dominated by greed. No other value seems to matter more than the self-centered greed that drives people to have more and more for them beyond what is reasonable and without having the greater picture of our society in mind. I feel that for the most part we have morally failed as a society and hope that we might come to a turning point some day in the near future, but I am not certain if we will. Short term thinking. Hand in hand with the greedy attitude comes a short term perspective. Corporate America with its focus on quarterly results over long term success has proven that many decisions makers in this world have lost such crucial things like vision, long term sustainable planning and thinking or even keeping the long term effects of their decisions in mind. In Germany we have a saying 'after me the flood to destroy everything.' And I feel that many decision makers in politics and economy follow this saying more than those who apply long term vision. Environmental indifference. I am shocked at how we treat our resources and how our society has developed a sense of entitlement to the environment. I think that we face the challenge to change this attitude and improve how we live in this highly competitive world. Globalization has leveled the playing field as the famous author Friedman states and we now live in a world of high competition among us. While I think that competition can help us to improve or even excel in what we do, I also think that many people in our world struggle with dealing with this kind of competition. As MBA students I think we should foster healthy constructive and friendly competition and I try to challenge myself through competition to be the best I can. On the other hand I believe that many people struggle to deal with a highly competitive world and I view it as a moral challenge to our society to deal with this problem. I certainly don't mean that competition should be eliminated. In Germany for example we have a society where the lack of competition and the lack of pressure has led to many problems such as people abusing the social system for their own benefit and an unwillingness to work hard and a belief of entitlement to wealth without work. On the other hand we witness people who struggle to do everything they can and yet unable to make it in this world we created. As a society we need to find the balance and improve away from cut throat competition to a more constructive way of helping each other improve ourselves. Unwillingness to make changes. I think that our society could be so much better off if we were willing to change. I think that quite often the changes are easy to identify and solutions easy to be found, but often so hard to implement. I believe that our world recognizes the challenges but we seem unwilling to make the necessary changes to resolve them: reforming the financial system, committing to environmental improvements, changing the way companies treat employees but also employees changing their work attitude, the list of examples is long, the solution often rather obvious and the occurring changes too often zero."

Professor Meyer: "Thank you. Those certainly are important concerns and insights. Next."

Student: "Teamwork. How much work each person needs to turn in or if one teammate decides to slack then who needs to pick up the work. Cheating during exam. If a student cheats and another student knows, what should he or she do? Tell the professor or let it go. Copying homework, even though some professors allow working together for homework. Computer usage to get answers/additional information. If the class is curved then do you teach your friends to help them or not. Passing answers around after a quiz/exam to others in a different session. Self-interest or interest for the company. Stealing from the office such as paper, whiteout and office supplies. Using company resources for personal gain. Working hours. Push workload to subordinates or other employees. Extended break lunch time. Do things socially responsible or as long as it cheaper. Use company credit card for business dinner when its dinner with people unrelated to work. Have someone clock in before you arrive. Push responsibility to others. Wasting resources when you can recycle or reuse. Driving to work when you can commute with public transportation or carpool."

Professor Meyer: "Thank you. More good topics for us to explore. Next."

Student: "Balancing compassion with professionalism. Disclosure, the differences between what I legally have to disclose and what I morally should disclose. Using nepotism to get ahead, when does that become unethical or is this business as usual. Are we more obligated to friends when conducting business even when they are in the wrong, even when friends are dragging your business down? With a soft economy it seems I have less leeway to show lenience to friends in business. Taking care of the poor and needy vs. capitalism and relationship between the two; public relations for greed operations and charitable causes. Protecting the environment. How does business impact the community; obligations to the global community. Cultural differences that create maligned moral difference, but neither is really in the wrong. Just different ways of seeing."

Professor Meyer: "Thank you. Next."

Student: "Taking the easy way out of things. Telling a white lie to avoid conflict. Following behavior I would not do myself but since it is in the workplace I feel obligated to. Greed versus want to be the best at whatever it might be. Genetics, human cloning and topics within this arena. Poverty, slavery, and human rights. Corporate greed. Materialistic society. World peace dictatorships."

Professor Meyer: "Thank you. Next."

Student: "How much is enough. When it comes to money, cars, gadgets, free time etc. how much is suitable for leading a well-balanced life, prosperous lifestyle. If an annual salary of $500K is sufficient for my needs is there any reason to trade free time and relaxation for more? How can I successfully balance life and work? Where is the tipping point between the responsibilities of work and the pleasure of life? Should I work more to offer my wife and children tangible prosperity? Or would additional family time be more beneficial for their wellbeing? How much should I give back to my church, community, friends and family? Since I am fundamentally opposed increasing government funded entitlement programs how much money and time should I donate in order to personally help those in need? As only one individual, how can I effectively assist these people? Should I choose a rewarding career that pays less or a taxing career that pays more? Because I have a wide range of skills and interests, should I choose to pursue a career path that offers limited pay but unlimited satisfaction or a career path that offers unlimited pay but limited satisfaction? How much should the government help the underprivileged? Although I do not see the utility in unnecessarily supporting capable individuals there is undoubtedly some level of assistance the government can offer to those who are truly underprivileged, incapable or downtrodden? How should the government decide who is truly in need. How can it effectively help?

How much responsibility should business have for addressing social desires? Should companies such as Exxon be forced to pay windfall taxes for performing above corporate standards and social expectations? Should there be a mandatory balance between corporate responsibility and social welfare? Who decides which moral and ethical code should take precedent? Until the middle part of the 20th century it was readily acknowledged that good/bad and right/wrong in America was defined by Judeo Christian morality. Although I personally subscribe to these beliefs, how does society balance the effects of a melting pot of varying moral and ethical ideas? Should politicians and business captains always reveal the whole truth, even when it may place the country or company in peril? The U.S Constitution was penned in total secrecy in a crowded room in Philadelphia. Yet today, the media and segments of society ceaselessly demand total transparency in every arena from congressional breakfast foods to CEO health records to detailed war strategy. How much should individuals in positions of power be required to disclose?"

Professor Meyer: "Thank you. We only have time for a couple more. Next."

Student: "Fairness e.g. preference in job and work. Respect toward others. Brutality and violence in computer games and on the street. Truthfulness. Exploitation of workers and the environment. Betrayal of confidence. Unfair competition. Respect towards other people e.g. teachers, elderly, races."

Professor Meyer: "Thank you. Next."

Student: "Viewing our society as unfair playing field. I tend to view education as the great equalizer and think that everyone has the same opportunities if they would work for them, but under the surface I know this isn't true. Judging others upon their accomplishments/education alone. I tend to view other people that are more similar to me in a positive light and people less similar to me in a more negative light. What duties do I owe my parents? My parents have done a lot to prepare me for success and I wonder if in return I should take their location in account when I decide where geographically to start my career? Viewing those close to me as more important than others. I believe very strongly in supporting those who are close to me, but at the same time feel no obligation to help those outside the small circle of my life. Helping someone I know is important to me, helping my community is not.

Trapped by unfounded Religious beliefs. Religion causes a tremendous amount of hate, violence and oppression throughout the world. It also blinds people to some of the harder realities of life.

Lack of Education. Education is vitally important to the improvement of not only individuals, but to the world in general. How to motivate less fortunate people to work, to better themselves is a challenge. Lack of commitment, motivation and passion in life. Too many people are content with the status quo and don't live their life to their fullest. Becoming tolerant of differences in societies. Our global world is bringing many different types of people together from many different backgrounds and cultures. Lack of integrity in daily life. Values and character are important for people to have and benefit the society at large."

Professor Meyer: "Thank you, unfortunately that's all the time we have for today. To those who did not get a chance to present their papers, rest assured I will read them before our next class. To those who presented I couldn't help but sense that many of your concerns stem from a struggle to reconcile what you are brought up to believe, against the hypocrisy of what you perceive to be practiced. By a show of hands how many feel that's an issue?"

All hands go up.

Professor Meyer: "It is my commitment to you that by the end of this Course we will have explored that issue and those presented in your papers sufficiently enough for you to reconcile them for yourself.

One more thing. Before you leave I want to remind you to check the Course Website each week for the reading and journal assignments, along with class notes. The journal assignments due for next week are entitled, 'Not Spending One Cent for a Day' and 'Documenting Every Cent You Spend in a Day'. Both are to be presented for discussion during our next Class entitled Thoughts on Wealth. I look forward to seeing you then. Class dismissed."

Acquiring Wealth, Power, Success, Morally and Ethically (AWPSME)

CLASS TWO

THOUGHTS ON WEALTH

Professor Meyer: "Good afternoon. It's good to be with you again. Before we review your journal assignment for today, let's talk about the concept of wealth. In last week's class most if not all of you, said you wanted to become wealthy yet weren't sure how much money you needed to achieve that goal; that is to say, when enough would be enough.

Let's assume for the sake of exploring this question that the attributes of those who are wealthy are the ones provided in your text book *The Millionaire Next Door*. Who can recall what those are?"

Student: "Being able to maintain your current lifestyle for years without earning even one month's pay."

Professor Meyer: "That's more a benchmark, I'm looking for attributes."

Student: "According to the authors, the prime attributes of most wealthy people are: 'That they live well below their means. That they allocate their time, energy and money efficiently in ways conducive to building wealth. That they believe financial independence is more important than displaying high social status. That their parents did not provide economic outpatient care. That their adult children are economically self-sufficient. That they are proficient in targeting market opportunities. And 'that they chose the right occupation.'"

Student: "I found it interesting that the authors said if you want to become financially independent you must first ask yourself if you really want to become financially independent. Interesting, because I assumed everybody would like to become financially independent. But then they followed this up with the question, 'Are you and your family willing to reorient your lifestyle to achieve this goal; including the discipline, sacrifice and hard work?' We've always heard that to succeed you must being willing to work hard, but nothing about 'reorienting your lifestyle' and that intrigued me."

Professor Meyer: "These are important statements. Some years ago a writer published a popular book on how to pick up girls. In it, the author made a point of saying if you want to be successful the first thing you have to do is ask yourself if you really want to pick up girls. Given the book's targeted readership of single boys and men, the assumption was of course they wanted to pick up girls otherwise why would they be reading the book? Yet the author knew intuitively or from experience or research, many likely assumed they wanted to pick up girls because as single boys and men they had been acculturated to believe that's what they were supposed to do and likely never gave it a second thought. He knew, as the authors of *The Millionaire Next Door* knew, without a deep personal commitment you would likely not succeed. That without this deep commitment you would likely not do that which it takes to achieve the goal. To this point I remember seeing a cartoon depicting a street beggar eying a rich man driving by in a Rolls Royce. The capture read 'I'd give ten dollars to be one of those millionaires.' So let's see how much are you willing to give?"

Student: "That's a good question. While I want to become wealthy and financially independent I also want a work/ life balance with time for a family and a home and children and be able to travel."

Student: "I'm prepared to give it my all for at least five or ten years, but if I haven't made it by then I doubt I will want to spend the rest of my life working eighteen hour days."

Student: "It's a tough question and I don't think I know the answer. Yes, I want to succeed in the business world, but at some point I want to be a stay at home mom and provide a good life for my children."

Professor Meyer: "Well all of you are in luck, because the formula to achieve financial wealth and independence that we are going to explore today is so simple every one of you can achieve it and still have a good work/life balance. I personally have used the formula throughout my life and can tell you it works. It is the same formula revealed in your Course text books *The Millionaire Next door* and "*Stop Acting Rich*" among others. Who can tell me what that formula is?"

Student: "Spend less than you make. Save what you don't spend. Invest it conservatively. And avoid the temptation to waste money on things you cannot afford. Don't run up credit cards and other debt. Don't spend money you don't have on things that will not be worth what you end up paying for them. And, if you do purchase something, it should either be an appreciating asset, in other words, worth more after you buy it, increases in value over time, or be something that makes you money when you own it and/or as you use it.'"

Professor Meyer: "Yes, thank you; well read. It is that simple. Yet according to Forbes Magazine, ninety percent of the world's population do not have enough savings to cover a five hundred dollar emergency? Think about that, ninety percent and only five hundred dollars! How many of you have access to five hundred dollars right now today if you needed it to cover an emergency?"

All hands go up.

Professor Meyer: "You see you are already wealthier than ninety percent of the world. Yet how many of you consider yourselves wealthy?"

No hands go up.

Professor Meyer: "Did it surprise you to know that most if not all of you, given your resources, are very likely in the top ten percent of the wealthiest people on the planet? Additionally, some of you given your family resources, are very likely in the top five percent of the wealthiest people on the planet. And some of you may also be in the top one percent of the wealthiest people on the planet. Sharia, please Google the question 'how much money does take to be in the top percent of wealth in the world' and read what you find."

Sharia: "According to Credit Suisse, 'a net worth of Ninety three thousand, one hundred and seventy dollars U.S. is enough to make you richer than ninety percent of the people around the world.' You need significantly less to be among the global fifty percent. If you have just four thousand two hundred ten dollars to your name you are still richer than half the world's residents. And it only takes a net worth of eight hundred seventy one thousand, three hundred twenty dollars, to join the global one percent."

Professor Meyer: "Thank you. Of course that is in terms of net worth, how about in terms of annual income?"

Sharia: "Here's a Pew Research Center finding: 'People who are middle income globally speaking, live on ten to twenty dollars a day, which translates to an annual income of about $14,600 to $29,200 for a family of four. The other four income groups are defined as follows: The poor live on two dollars or less daily, low income on two to ten dollars a day, upper-middle income on twenty to fifty dollars a day, and high income on more than fifty dollars a day.'

I also found this. By global standards, America's middle class is really, really rich. According to the World Bank, to make it into the richest one percent globally all you need is an annual income of around $24,000. The average family in the United States has more than three times the income of those living in poverty in America and nearly fifty times that of the world's poorest. Many of America's and the West's ninety nine percenters are really one percenters on a global level in terms of annual income."

Professor Meyer: "Thank you Sharia. So according to the data Sharia found, give or take the numbers, most if not all of you, are in or will be in, the top one percent of the world in terms of income, and at least in the top ten percent in your own countries, yet you want more. Part of the reason for this is you are likely identifying with the CEOs of Wall Street and Silicon Valley and not the ninety nine percent of the world. I'm not saying this to judge you, but only for perspective."

Student: "As you said Professor, wealth is a state of mind. To some I'm wealthy, compared to others, I'm barely getting by."

Dennis Torres

Professor Meyer: "So wealth then has at least two compo-
nents, on one hand a certain level of resources and on the
other the ability to appreciate those resources."

Student: "But professor it's easy to say I'm in the top percent in terms of resources and here's the perfect wealth
building formula, but I have nearly a hundred thousand
dollars of student loan debt. How can I spend less with that
debt hanging over my head?"

Professor Meyer: "It may surprise you, but that is not a major
obstacle. Let's look at your journal assignment documenting what you spent your money on in one random day."

Student: Breakfast at home: Cereal $2.00; Starbucks on
campus $4.45; lunch at school cafeteria $11; snack at the
school cafeteria $5.00; gas for the car $26.00; dinner with
friends $39.49."

Professor Meyer: "How often do you buy Starbucks?"

Student: "Nearly every day."

Professor Meyer: "Using round numbers that's close to six
dollars a day pre-tax. If you stopped buying Starbucks and
took advantage of the free coffee in the student lounge or
brought your own from home and invested the money you
saved, it could eventually pay off that student loan. One of
our guest speakers in last semester's class, was an investment banker who told the story of how when he and his

70

wife married they had very little money and she use to buy a Starbucks every day. So he told her if she gave up Starbucks for a few years he would invest the money and the return on it would give her a free Starbucks every day for the rest of her life. Look too at your other expenditures, aside from gas, which could be reduced by carpooling or possibly taking public transportation, they add up to about fifty five dollars whereas if you prepared food at home you could likely cut that in half or less and be well on your way to eliminating your student loan without having to increase your income. Let's look at some more examples of daily expenditures. Who wants to go next?"

Student: Groceries $43.18; gas $36.99; cafeteria lunch $14.18; movie and popcorn $11.59; dinner out $35.40."

Professor Meyer: "I guess you didn't have time to study that day. If you had, you could have saved a lot of money."

Laughter from the class.

Professor Meyer: "Now let's assume all of you had set a goal to become wealthy and were willing do what was necessary to achieve that goal, what could you have done otherwise?"

Student: "Brought lunch from home, watch a movie on TV and cook dinner at home."

Professor Meyer: "Exactly! And how much do you estimate you would have saved to invest?"

Student: "Maybe fifty dollars that day alone."

Professor Meyer: "And you would have had to earn something more than sixty or seventy dollars to have that fifty. Consider too, that just fifty dollars a week invested over ten years would return to you more than $38,000 and in twenty years more than $114,000 using only a modest interest component. And not only that, you would not have missed the money."

Student: "That's amazing."

Professor Meyer: "It's a small example of what it takes to create wealth and why you must ask yourself if you really want to become wealthy. In the interest of time I'll assume the rest of you have similar expenditures and we'll move on.
    Who can tell me, perhaps you finance concentration majors, what's worth more a penny earned or a penny saved?"

Student: "A penny earned?"

Professor Meyer: "Why do you say that?"

Student: "Because it's new money."

Professor Meyer: "I say a penny saved. Can anyone tell me why?"

Student: "Because it's saved and you can invest it?"

Professor Meyer: "I gave you a hint just a few minutes ago. It's because a penny saved is after tax money where a penny earned is pre-tax money. Here's another way of understanding this, if you buy something for a hundred dollars you have to earn perhaps twenty percent or more to pay for it depending on your Federal and State income tax brackets so thinking you only paid one hundred dollars is flawed accounting. If you save money on a purchase through wise shopping e.g. by price comparison or cents-off/dollars-off coupons or waiting for a sale, the money you saved is after federal and state taxes, in addition you paid less sales tax which could add up to even more.

Here's yet another way of looking at this. The work of earning the penny saved is already done. To earn another penny you would have to work. By reducing the money you spend you can put it to work for you and reduce your need to work. Do you see what I mean?"

Students collectively: "Yes."

Professor Meyer: "How many of you shop with 'cents-off/dollars-off coupons, the kind you see in the weekly supermarket advertisements and online?"

No hands go up.

Professor Meyer: "How much would you guess the average cents-off/dollars-off coupon shopper saves over a lifetime?"

Student: "Maybe ten thousand dollars?"

Professor Meyer: "According to online sources on grocery cents-off coupons alone, you will save well over $100,000 dollars and that's tax free money. What demographic shopper would you guess uses these coupons more, low income shoppers, middle income shoppers or high income shoppers?"

Student: "I would assume low income shoppers because they have less money to spend, but suspect since you asked the question that it might be the opposite?"

Professor Meyer: "According to the Internet, high income shoppers like those who live in upscale neighborhoods use grocery cents-off coupons considerably more than low income shoppers. Why do you suppose that is?"

Student: "Because they are more money centric than low income shoppers who have less money?"

Student: "Or it could be the stores in lower income neighborhoods don't offer as many cents-off coupons, because there's little competition and they don't have to?"

Professor Meyer: "According to Internet data it's because they are money centric; they know and respect the value of money. While I haven't researched it, I suspect the lack of competition you cite might also be factor. The point of mentioning this disparity however, is to illustrate that wealth builders are typically money conscious and frugal. Here are some other things found on the Internet that money conscious, frugal wealth builders do. A few of them have already been mentioned, but bear repeating. Note too, that the numbers are not adjusted for inflation which would make them a lot higher.

1. 'A sandwich at a retail store or restaurant can cost $5 to $10 a day. That might not seem like much, but over a year, spending that every work day puts your annual expenditure into four figures. If you instead bring food from home, you can feed yourself for half as much. If you invest those savings—of up to $35 a week, or about $1,800 a year you'd have the tidy sum of about **$84,000** after 25 years.

2. Join Super Market loyalty programs. A shopper could probably save $25 a week on groceries. That adds up to more than $1,000 a year or **$60,000** over that 25 years.

3. Take advantage of full time student discounts available at many restaurants and retailers usually offering up to ten percent.

4. Switch to a cashback credit card that offers generous cashback rewards then charge as many regular expenses as you can: Groceries, gas, utilities and restaurants, everything you can think of. Make sure though, that you pay off your credit card bill in full at the end of the month. Paying interest on a balance will wipe out any rewards you'd have earned and very likely cost you more than you saved. That works out to $30 a month or nearly **$18,000** over 25 years.

5. Shop for Home Telecom Service. Many areas have more than one company that provides cable TV, internet and landline services. Sometimes there's a big price difference between them. The potential 25-year benefit: nearly **$12,000**

6. Consider Switching Mobile Services too. Those savings would deliver a multi-year benefit of more than **$3,000**.

7. Bank fees. Look beyond the balance on your bank account statements and you may be surprised at the number of fees you are paying. A few smart practices can help limit these, including withdrawing cash only at fee-free ATMs, carefully coordinating your available funds with any checks you write to avoid costly overdraft fees, and using credit cards and free P2P payments apps like Zelle to reduce your need for cash withdrawals. On average, Americans pay a fairly modest $97.80 a year in fees on their checking account, according to the Consumer Finance Protection Bureau. However, there are many no-fee checking accounts and those that offer reduced fees depending on customer usage. NerdWallet recently looked at some of the best no-fee accounts. Over 25 years, an account that costs only two-thirds of the average account would earn you about **$3,500**.

8. Reduce Your Insurance Premiums. Review your homeowner's and auto insurance policies at least every year for changes that could save you money. Even if you don't opt for an entirely new carrier a host of moves can help you reduce premiums. For

example, consolidating all the policies you hold with one company typically earns a discount of between 5% and 25% on each. If you're insuring an older car, its optional collision and comprehensive coverage may no longer make financial sense if the maximum claim payout (the vehicle's value minus your deductible) drops to 10% or less of the total annual premium for those two coverages. And for almost any insurance policy, increasing your deductible almost invariably reduces the premium—and, of course, alters your financial risk. That difference, of about $450 a year, would add up to about **$22,000** over 25 years.

9. Now here's a big one. Enroll in Your Employer's Retirement Savings Program and any other tax deferred or tax free programs offered like HSA health savings programs. The closest thing to free savings are the matching contributions many employers offer for company-sponsored 401(k), Simple IRA and other salary deferral feature plans. Employers who offer these perks typically add up to half of your contribution to the plan.

    If you're hesitating to join the company plan, then, you're losing out on not only the benefit of tax-deferred retirement savings of your own but in having those contributions supercharged by your employer. Even invested as per a (conservative) formula, those contributions could create a fund totaling millions of dollars after 25 years. The employer contributions alone would have contributed a significant amount to that fund of money you would not have had otherwise.

10. Refinance your mortgage when rates are lower. I've done this in addition to making additional payments over those called for and have saved hundreds of thousands of after tax dollars. Reducing your interest rate not only saves money but increases the rate at which you build equity in your home. For example, a 30-year fixed-rate mortgage with a $100,000 principal remaining at an interest rate of 9% has a principal and interest payment of $804.62 a month. That same loan at 4.5% reduces your payment to $506.69—for a monthly savings of $297.93 (current rates are near historic lows of 3.125% as of December 2021). Those savings, over 25 years and invested at 5%, would add up to $175,260. The one-time cost to refinance is between 3% and 6%, or between $3,000 and $6,000 for our example. That would still result in a lifetime benefit of at least **$169,000**. But also be aware that each time you refinance in the early years most of your monthly payments are going toward interest charges rather than principal reduction; the opposite is true during the later years.

11. Optimize Timing for Big-ticket Purchases. Substantial savings are possible if you're willing and able to wait for seasonal sales and clearances on big buys. Those optimal times fall into two basic categories. The first are major holidays, almost all of which are now an excuse for retailers to hold 'sales events'

of some kind. The end-of-year holiday season is the best example beginning with Black Friday sales the day after Thanksgiving. Carefully researched, Black Friday buys can often, though not invariably, be the best of the year, especially in electronics categories such as TVs and computers. Categories featured in the sales on holiday weekends include appliances on Memorial Day, furniture on July 4th, and mattresses on Labor Day.

The other major sale opportunity is to snap up older items as the New Year's models begin to arrive, or as seasons end. Buying last year's stock does however, mean selection may have dwindled and you sacrifice acquiring the latest features and technology—but those advances are fairly incremental given the maturity of most big-ticket categories. Optimal categories and times to take advantage of model-year and seasonal changes include cars in October and November, grills in September, and winter sports gear and clothing in March and April.

12. Earn More Interest on Your Savings with online super savings accounts. Saving money is only part of it. When you invest savings instead of spending them, you can at least double your returns over 25 years, due to the power of compounding. You'll also get easy access to simple transfers and auto-deposits.

13. The Bottom Line. All of these savings strategies and others readily available, will likely amount to an impressive nest egg of potentially millions of dollars

over twenty five years or so. And for the most part, with fairly minimal sacrifice to you.'

Question, how much money would you guess you would have to earn yearly in order to save enough to acquire wealth?"

Student: "In this economy maybe seventy to one hundred thousand a year?"

Student: "I'll say at least two hundred thousand dollars a year."

Professor Meyer: "It might surprise you to know that people who have earned a minimum wage or were low wage earners their entire lives have used the same wealth building formula we have discussed here, that is to spend less and save and invest more, to successfully acquire wealth. If you Google the subject you will find many stories about them. Here are a few.

'Her name was Rose, a single woman who earned a very modest salary. She bought an old house, hired homeless people to help her fix it up and rented it out. The renters paid her mortgage on the house. Later she bought another by using not only the new house as collateral, but the equity in her other house. She rented that one too.

In time her real estate holdings grew. She always hired homeless people from a downtown shelter to work on her houses. Everyone knew her and they all did their work to the best of their ability.

When Rose passed away, her estate was worth over six million dollars. The entire estate was turned over to her son to manage and according to its terms he could keep the profits to pay him for managing it, then when he dies, the entire estate goes to the homeless shelter.

Another such story is about a man named Ronald Read who worked as a minimum wage gas station attendant and a JC Penny janitor in Brattleboro, Vermont. He lived frugally yet comfortably below his means and invested in the stock market. When he died at age ninety four he was worth eight million dollars and left five million of that to the local hospital where stopped each day to buy coffee at their coffee shop; he said it had the best coffee in town. He drove an old Toyota and was known to walk blocks away from his destination to avoid having to put money in parking meters.' By the way I do the same thing. Instead of paying money I get the pleasure of some stress relieving exercise and of being outside in nature. And when I go to a shopping center instead of driving around and around polluting the environment, wasting time and gas and getting stressed out trying to find a parking space as close to the entrance as possible I park at the first spot I come to and enjoy the walk.

Then there's Leonard Gigowski a butcher and grocer in Milwaukee, Wisconsin who lived a full life. He loved ballroom dancing and built a dance floor in the basement of his modest home. He also loved racing pigeons and had a pigeon coop in his yard. Early in his life he decided that he wanted to make an impact on the world by setting up a scholarship fund to benefit his high school and when he died in 2015 at age 90, he left that fund thirteen million dollars.'

I'll add, that when you have a purpose in life other than yourself there is no such thing as sacrifice and no such thing as feeling unfulfilled. When my wife and I started a charitable NGO I put my business on hold and worked eighteen hour days for almost five years without pay to get it off the ground. When I needed to get back to earning a living it felt like a giant step down even though I enjoyed my work.

And finally, 'Margaret Southern a special needs teacher from Greenville, South Carolina who died in 2012 at age ninety four. All her life she loved animals and when she died she left half of her almost eight million dollar estate to the local Humane Society and most of the other half to the Community Foundation of Greenville to benefit children's education. She also left some money to friends and family.'

There are countless stories of low and minimum wage earners who amassed great wealth. And it's not just low earners who choose to give meaning to their lives by living frugally so that they can help others, here's the story of a self-made billionaire couple who did the same.

Chuck Feeney the cofounder of Duty Free Shoppers, the stores you find in airports, was worth eight billion dollars, that's with a 'B', when he declared 'I want to die broke.' He and his wife amassed those billions while living a life of monk like frugality. According to an article in Forbes Magazine he pioneered the idea of 'Giving While Living' which advocates donating most of your fortune to charity while you are still alive so you have control of where it goes and can see the results. It took a few decades but the eighty nine year old finally succeeded and said he couldn't be happier. According to Forbes magazine he set aside two million dollars of his billions for his and his wife's retirement.

Chuck Feeney and his wife are not alone. There are countless stories too of high net worth people like the Feeneys' who lived below their means and created wealth not to lavish it on themselves but to benefit others. As a benchmark to living simply, realize that each and every one of you enjoy comforts considerably greater than the richest of the rich in the days before running water, indoor plumbing and electricity; something that did not exist even in Los Angeles a mere one hundred and sixty years ago and still doesn't in much of the world. One of my good friends great, great, great grandfather immigrated to Los Angeles in the mid eighteen hundreds when the total population was less than two thousand four hundred people. The streets were rutted dirt roads littered with trash and dead animals as there were no municipal services like trash collection. There was also no electricity and no running water. For a fee someone delivered a bucket of water to your house each day, only the water came from the L.A. river where animals grazed and defecated so it was not really drinkable; for that you had to rely on collected rain water, a well, or drink wine. Restaurants had dirt floors and cooked outback in the open air and the dishes and utensils were not washed but wiped with a dirty rag. Even when his grandfather became super wealthy he did not have the comforts you are living with today.

Now's a good time to hear about your journal assignment of '*Not Spending one Cent for a Day*' along with the suggestion of opening a linked account to automatically transfer the money saved into that account for later investment. Who wants to start off?"

Student: "This exercise was one of the most rewarding financial experiments of my life. When I first read the assignment I expected it would be an interesting assignment, but not a life-changing process. However, as I began the day with a mindset determined to not spend any money, the frivolous breath of my usual spending habits started to become apparent: Four dollars wasted on coffee, six dollars wasted on snacks, ten dollars wasted on non-sale grocery items. When I started to appreciate this waste, it became clear how easy it would be to amass large long-term savings and investments.

Assuming I could save and invest even five dollars per day invested monthly at a modest eight percent over ten years, I could amass just under fifty thousand dollars, and over twenty years I could amass a whopping nearly three hundred and fifty thousand dollars all with only five dollars per day! Armed with this information I opened up a savings and investment account with Charles Schwab. On the first of every month my accounts are set to automatically transfer one hundred fifty dollars from checking into this alternative saving account. Simultaneously, this money is set to be invested in broad-based mutual funds with hopes to efficiently capitalize on money that used to be applied to frivolous activities."

Professor Meyer: "Excellent! Congratulations and thanks for that report. Who wants to go next?"

Student: "During my evening lecture the cafeteria was closed so it was relatively easy to resort to drinking from the water fountain and not spending any money. Nonetheless, after going through the experiment the insights were valuable. Especially the fact that I didn't mind at all to replace the usual soft drink with water from the fountain. It made me question the necessity of buying these drinks in the future. I feel I should repeat the experiment at another time when not spending would be even harder to achieve. For example on the weekend where spending money is frequently associated with having fun. It would be interesting to see whether the degree of happiness and fulfillment declines when being committed to a non-spending policy for one of those days. Based on the Monday experience I would expect a positive outcome and even more valuable insights."

Professor Meyer: "Thank you, good report. Did you open that linked account?

Student: "Not yet, but I will."

Professor Meyer: "Don't forget. Next."

Student: "This exercise was definitely a challenge for me and I was unable to plan things out well enough during the last week to not spend in a day. However, I have had a few days over the last few months where I haven't spent a cent. The interesting part of that experience and the biggest surprise is that on those days of not spending I didn't feel truly deprived or didn't feel that my well-being was adversely affected. Although those days happened by accident, they showed me that it is possible to live that way as long as you are willing to make certain adjustments.

What's important about this exercise is that it teaches us to focus on what matters, friends, nature, relationships, and fulfilling experiences. Money does have some role to play in some of those things, but it is by no means critical to any of them. Thinking ahead and thinking of what really matters are the concepts that help me come to grips with not spending and realize that I can live just fine on those days that I cut back on spending."

Professor Meyer: "Thank you for those good insights. Next."

Student: "Although this exercise turned out to be more difficult than I originally expected, I really enjoyed completing it. I prepared myself for the day of not spending (Monday) by having groceries and gas in my car; I figured that if I had those necessities, not spending money would be easy. I have one class on Mondays and usually I buy something to snack on or drink during both of the breaks. However, this day I brought both of these items from home. After I got home from class, I realized that I needed some things from Rite-Aid, but stopped myself from going. Usually, I would have gone and not even thought about how much I was spending because I consider items like Q-tips and tissues as necessities. But since I couldn't go out and spend money I used what I had in the house for what I needed. When it was time to eat, I wanted to order out instead of cooking, but yet again, I could not do so. Instead, I cooked some of the food I bought and ended up eating a lot healthier than I would have if I had eaten out.

This exercise really helped me to realize how carelessly I spend money. I take my ATM card out without even thinking about what I am doing. I think it makes it ever easier to spend a lot because I'm not actually handling cash in my hands so I don't know exactly how much I've spent until I look at my account online. I think I will start taking out a certain amount of cash every week and only allowing myself to spend that certain amount, no exceptions.

I started giving myself manicures and pedicures that will help me save so much money and make me realize even deeper how much I don't need. I'm sure once I start with this awareness it will snowball and I will see how much I can really save by cutting down my spending on needless items that I used to consider necessities. I agree with you that this is real power. I want to have full control of my spending habits and not be swayed by the media or by my circle of friends to just spend and spend and spend. I know that this one day of not spending money is just the first step, but I am really happy that I took this class and made that step already before I got too old and too set in my ways."

Professor Meyer: "Thank you. Those are some good insights for all of us. If you haven't done it yet, remember to open that linked account so you can transfer money from your regular savings account to it for investing. Next."

Student: "What this showed me is that in general I've been very unaware of not only my cash and credit card expenses, but also the consumption of things I already have which leads to more purchasing to replace those products. This experiment combined with the daily tracking of expenses brought about a new, different level of awareness that I am not used to. I just hope that I can continue to keep this in the front of my mind when I make purchasing decisions in the future."

Professor Meyer: "Thank you. Next."

Student: "When doing this exercise I was curious if I would actually forget about the money when I put it into the bank account. Two days after putting the money into the account I truly felt like I forgot about it altogether and came to the conclusion I could do it again. In short, the exercise was good for me mentally from the aspect that it separated the impulse of wanting to make unneeded purchases. Purchases just start adding up and people don't realize what they are spending their money on."

Professor Meyer: "How true. Thank you. Next."

Student: "The experiment of not spending money for an entire day was very freeing. I chose Wednesday because it is a day full of classes and I'm busy and productive all day. I love the feeling of going through the day and realizing I'm not spending money on groceries, tea breaks, or gasoline. To me saving even five dollars is a success. This is why I come to school prepared not to spend money. I did this by bringing my own lunch prepared from home and other needed food for the day. I also brought my own tea bag so all I relied on was free hot water from the cafeteria. I figured if I can avoid paying for cafeteria food during the week I can save at least a hundred dollars a month that's two months of Internet bills or two evenings out with my girlfriend. I took your suggestion of opening up a linked account and set it up to automatically get five dollars each week when it grows to five hundred or a thousand I can then invest it. After graduation when I get a job I will put more money into it.

This exercise has helped me to define a life investment plan. I foresee myself saving and investing money my entire life going forward."

Professor Meyer: "Thank you. To leave enough time for a discussion on frugality and our guest speaker we'll have to stop here, but I appreciate the presentations and look forward to reading the remainder of your journal assignments.

When you hear the word frugality what comes to your mind?"

Student: "Being cheap?"

Student: "A euphuism for being cheap."

Student: "Thrifty?"

Professor Meyer: "According to the online Dictionary, *cheap* in the context of this discussion, means 'stingy or miserly', while *frugal* means 'economical in use or expenditure; prudently saving or sparing; not wasteful.'

Here's what else you will find online about the subject. 'Cheap is about spending less. Frugal is about prioritizing your spending so that you can acquire or achieve the things you really care about. Frugality is about spending wisely; knowing the difference between a want and a need; and understanding the difference between money saved and money earned; and between short term desires and long term goals. Frugality is about living well on less and requires self-discipline. For some people it's a difficult sacrifice for others, it's a pleasurable journey in simplification where fulfillment results from redirecting earned income toward financial freedom rather than squandering it on spending. It's not uncommon for extreme frugalists to save 70% of income and achieve financial independence in less than ten years, but it's not everyone's cup of tea. In short, you must create a gap between how much you earn and how much you spend that results in savings to invest for growth and additional income.

The twin themes of spending less and making more are not mutually exclusive, but they do require very different mindsets. One alternative is to raise the income side of the equation. The advantage to this approach is there is no theoretical limitation to how fast your wealth can grow because your earning capacity is unlimited.

Many wealth gurus teach the income side of the equation as the path to wealth; however, if you don't master the spending side of the equation, you still run a high risk of failure due to the all-too-common mistake of allowing spending to rise as fast as income.

The greatest wealth builders focus on both sides of the equation together. They maximize savings by controlling spending while growing income at the same time.

The quickest, most certain path to increased savings for investment is to focus on both saving money and earning more.

The third component is to invest wisely; it is also simple because everything you need to learn is available for free in the public domain. You don't have to take investment seminars or build extraordinary expertise. There are two well proven paths:

The first is *Stock/Bonds/Mutual Funds* so called 'Paper Assets' using conventional buy and hold strategy of investing in low cost index funds and proven asset allocation models. Suzie Orman a well-known financial advisor, author and investment guru says that 'the safest strategy is diversification in proven companies; small percentages of investment spread across those stocks and bonds.' Later in the Course we will have a guest speaker who will speak to you on this type of investment.

The other is *Real Estate*: Direct ownership of positive cash flow real estate in your local area. But you must educate yourself about the market place regarding industrial, commercial, residential, vacant land, development, location, trends, school districts, regulations, etc. And know that real estate investment is more active than passive and will likely require you to manage it or manage a manager, twenty four seven which also means you have a certain level of control in improving the returns unlike paper investments in companies over which you have little control and are comparatively management passive. Later in the Course we will have guest speakers who will speak to you on this type of investment.

Another strategy is one that I've heard many of you talking about and that is the overnight success strategy. I've heard some of you say post-graduation you want to develop an App or create a hedge fund or start a company then sell it with the end goal of becoming super wealthy before you turn thirty or maybe as late as thirty five then retire and travel around the world having a good time. Can it happen, sure, but despite what you've heard or read, the odds are against you. Typically those overnight successes are preceded by many years of hard times that often include multiple failures, and/or were blessed with an extraordinary occurrence of good fortune. This is true of the so called overnight successes of Gates, Jobs, Zuckerberg, Musk, Ford and Edison, who possessed brilliant minds and had a good deal of luck.

If you still want to pursue the idea of getting rich quick here are a few options I found on the Internet:

'Marry rich: Ethically and morally questionable at best and with lots of relationship down sides. *Lotteries:* Very, very, very low odds, but a big payoff. *Inheritance:* Probably not an option for some of you. *Various high and low risk illegal means.* I'll speak to a few of these to help you out. Now I'm not recommending you pursue any illegal or unethical means to acquire wealth, to the contrary I am advising strongly against this, but mention them because it is likely that as you pursue your careers certain temptations will likely present

themselves some disguised as not really illegal or unethical, but 'clever' or 'brilliant' or in the grey area between legal and illegal or somewhere between ethical and unethical. Remember from our introductory class that every action contains within it an inescapable consequence even if you don't get caught and nobody finds out about it. For those of you who don't care about the consequences here are two out of many, many low risk illegal, unethical ways to make a fast buck.

The first: Rent a house under an assumed identity and subsequently advertise it for rent to others at a below market competitive price. When prospective tenants start showing up have all of them fill out an application along with an application fee and credit check fee and shortly thereafter followed by a rental agreement with first and last month's rental deposit and do this to as many prospective tenants as you can before disappearing. This can be done to multiple residences simultaneously as well.

The second: Search public records for homes that are free and clear of liens then assume the identity of the owners and borrow money against the homes before disappearing. It will likely take many months before the true owner will even know what happened and likely never discover who did it. You can easily borrow hundreds of thousands of dollars per house and unlike robbing a bank there is little risk of getting caught or getting shot.

Both of these illegal, immoral, unethical schemes are in wide use every day. But remember despite the extremely

Dennis Torres

low risk of getting caught, that doesn't mean perpetrators escape the consequences. Take it from me there's no substitute for peace of mind.

In an upcoming class we will have a guest speaker, a contemporary of your generation, and like you brilliant and well educated, who found herself in federal prison after she crossed the line of ethics and legality in her career as an attorney.

A better strategy to becoming wealthy is by being a better person; being kind, respectful, fair, understanding, helpful, and empathetic and enjoying the consequences that come from this type of behavior. That doesn't mean you won't experience challenges that at times may feel like punishment, but in reality they are stepping stones moving you forward toward your goal. Are there any questions?"

Hearing none he continued.

Professor Meyer: "In summary, you may wonder when is best time for you to begin your journey toward achieving wealth and fulfillment. There is a wise saying often attributed to the Chinese philosopher Confucius that states, 'a journey of a thousand miles begins with a single step.' Meaning you start right where you are today by cultivating and activating the habits that serve your goals. Here are some suggestions including a few I've already mentioned, but bear repeating:

1. As I said many times, if you haven't already opened that high yield linked savings account so you can

regularly transfer money to it from your regular checking or savings accounts, do so today with the idea that it is untouchable except to invest for the future.

2. Regularly review you expenditures to make sure they meet your frugality test and eliminate any and all that are unnecessary. Than transfer the money you saved to your new linked account.

3. Cancel most if not all subscriptions and don't renew or purchase any more. In most cases the information you are paying for is readily available for free on the Internet, or underutilized or unneeded and a waste of your time. If you find you need something unavailable elsewhere, pay for it with the one-time fee.

4. Sell or give away unneeded, unused items that are cluttering your environment. This will not only provide you with money, but free up the time spent in dealing with them over and over in the future; even if it is only moving a box from here to there. Send any money you get to your linked account.

5. Pay off your debts especially high interest credit cards and don't charge anything you can't pay for in full when the bill comes due with exceptions for appreciating assets.

6. When you start working opt-in to your company's 401(k) and 457(b) and HSA, or any other tax advantaged saving vehicle available including an outside IRA. Make sure your contributions are automatic and never give a second thought to using

the money until you retire. Tax deferred (or in the case of an HSA, tax free) vehicles are excellent investments for wealth building.

7. If and when you have a mortgage, pay it off before it comes due by regularly adding an additional payment monthly, quarterly or annually. And consider refinancing when interests rates drop if it makes sense to do so considering refinancing costs and front loaded interest to principal payments. The after tax money you save will be astronomical.

8. Learn how to repair things. Tutorials are available throughout the Internet on sites such as YouTube. Not only will you save a lot of money over the years, but gain skills and personal satisfaction. Also, repair where it makes sense rather than replace and vice versa.

9. Consider the asset allocation and investment advice already covered in this lesson and that presented by our guest speakers throughout the Course.

10. Continue to develop your critical thinking skills through curiosity and questioning.

11. And here's a really big one. Become the 'go to person', the problem solver, and the person who can be depended upon to get the job done. Make your mantra *'consider it done.'* It will increase your job security and income immensely. More about this in next week's class *Thoughts on Power.* Are there any questions?"

Hearing none Professor Meyer continued.

Professor Meyer: "Let's take a ten minute break and when you return we'll hear from our guest speaker."

Following the break.

Professor Meyer: "Our guest speaker today Mr. Ahmad Ahmadi, immigrated to this Country from his native Iran with virtually no money, little to no command of the English language, and with a wife and three children to support. In less than a decade he became independently wealthy. In recounting his journey he will tell you how he did it and how you can do the same. Please give a warm welcome to Mr. Ahmad Ahmadi."

Following the applause.

Mr. Ahmadi: "Thank you professor Meyer and all of you for welcoming me to your class. I am truly humbled and honored to be here. In my former country of Iran I studied engineering and graduated with a Master's Degree. But when the revolution occurred I felt I had to leave everything behind and come to this country along with my wife who had a master's degree in chemistry and our three children, two girls and a boy all under the age of ten. When we arrived we had no money, no place to live, and did not know more than a few words of the language.

I got a job as dish washer in a restaurant and my wife got a job as a cook at a fast food restaurant where she prepared fried chicken. We worked different shifts so one of us could be at home with our children when they weren't in school. I was paid in cash because it was below minimum wage, and the restaurant where my wife worked let her take home some of the food left over at the end of the day which helped with our budget. After a few months when a waiter didn't show up I was given a chance to fill in for him and did such a good job was promoted full time as a waiter. The tips meant I had more income. In between lunch and dinner I volunteered to help out the owner doing everything I could to learn the business. I also enrolled in a course in restaurant management at the local junior college. After completing the course the owner of the restaurant promoted me to shift manager.

My wife and I saved every penny so we could to buy a house, but before we could buy a house we heard of a franchise restaurant that was in financial trouble. I went over and spoke with the owner and told him if I could turn the restaurant around so he could avoid bankruptcy and get nothing, would he sell it to me with no money down. He agreed and for the next seven months I worked night and day using what I had learned at my former restaurant and the Community college; many nights sleeping at the restaurant. When it started to make a profit the owner kept his word and sold it to me and my wife and we made payments to him. Later we heard of another restaurant in the franchise that was under performing and by then had enough money for a small down payment and a track record with the franchisor so we were able to take that one over too.

Eventually we had enough money to purchase a home. We could have purchased one in a first tier neighborhood, but decided it would be better for our children to live in a second tier neighborhood so they wouldn't be exposed to a high consumer lifestyle.

Not long after we purchased our home we opened a third restaurant with my wife's brother, but it failed due to problems involving the family relationship. The setback almost cost us our home and two other restaurants, but we learned a valuable lesson. Not to bring in a partner if you can avoid it, especially family. It also validated that we made a good choice not to purchase a home in a first tier neighborhood where our expenses would have been a lot higher and we might have lost everything. As I heard your professor say, it is best to live below your means so you not only have money to invest, but as a cushion against problems which will come no matter who you are or what you do.

Over the next couple of years we brought three more franchises, then saved enough money to buy a second house to rent out followed by more than twenty single family homes over the years which are all rentals. We chose single family homes because they are not subject to the same regulations that govern apartment buildings. We also purchased the land under our restaurants because successful restaurants can be forced out of business when leases are up and the landlord raises the rent.

From the time they were physically able our children worked in the restaurants to gain business experience and earn their own money. Today my son is a lawyer, one daughter is a doctor and the other a teacher. Thanks to the opportunities in this great Country, my wife and I are financially well off and never have to work another day if we choose not to, but we continue to work and live modestly with all the comforts life can provide. Our one daughter lives in Maine with her husband and our only grandchild so we are trying to get them to move back to Arizona by buying them a nice home. So that is our story. If you have any questions I will be happy to answer them as best I can. Thank you for listening to me."

Following applause.

Professor Meyer: "Thank you for sharing your journey. It's very inspirational. Are there any questions for Mr. Ahmadi?"

Student: "Yes. Mr. Ahmadi, you say you still live modestly, but I couldn't help notice in the parking lot you are driving a top of the line BMW."

Mr. Ahmadi: "Yes that is true. But first I must tell you I like to drive fast so I have a twelve cylinder BMW that sells for over one hundred thousand dollars and even though I can afford to buy a new one I bought it used for less than half that amount."

Student: "As long as we are on that subject I noticed your watch."

Mr. Ahmadi: "Let me tell you, I can afford any watch I want a Rolex, Patak Philip you can name it, even used they cost a lot of money, sometimes even more than new ones. The one I wear is a Seiko that cost less than one hundred fifty dollars. It's the same model Steve Jobs use to wear."

Student: "Mr. Ahmadi, thank you for sharing your story. It's one that is right out of our text books *The Millionaire Next Door* and *Stop Acting Rich*. But I would like to ask you, now that you have money do you still live in the same second tier neighborhood?"

Mr. Ahmadi: "Yes. We like our home and our neighbors and with the children gone the house is actually larger than we need. We have found that by living simply we gain a lot of freedom to enjoy the things that really matter like relationships, family and peace and quiet. There is a saying in the Iranian culture that translates to, *instead of wanting things you don't need you appreciate the things you do have.* My wife and our children feel very blessed to have so much we don't want for anything; we feel blessed by having the privilege to help others who are not so fortunate, not just by donating money, but our time and effort to help them better themselves."

Professor Meyer: "I promised Mr. Ahmadi I would have him out by three o'clock so we only have time for a few more questions."

Student: "Mr. Ahmadi, I'm just curious, do you and your wife ever splurge on anything frivolous and if so what is it?"

Mr. Ahmadi: "It's funny that you asked, because up to now we have not, but we are big fans of futbol, what is called here soccer, and are going to Brazil for the World Cup."

Professor Meyer: "Time for one more."

Student: "What advice other than what you have already offered can you give us to acquire wealth and have a successful life?"

Mr. Ahmadi: "Don't get side tracked by short term temptations; the kind that comes when people say you only live once. Keep your goals in mind. If you maintain focus on your goals time will be kind to you. Nothing good comes without a degree of stress and hard work."

Professor Meyer: "Thank you so much for sharing your inspirational story of success. Please know that it was not only appreciated, but I am certain it will change some lives for the better. We wish you and your wife a great well-deserved vacation to Brazil and hope that your favorite team wins. Let's have a show of appreciation for Mr. Ahmadi."

Following the applause Mr. Ahmadi leaves.

Professor Meyer: "Mr. Ahmadi has generously provided me with his email address in the event you have other questions.

A few more thoughts before we leave today. When Mr. Ahmadi talked about traveling to Brazil to see the World Cup Soccer games it reminded me that many if you are big sports fans and the sports merchandise you buy can cost hundred dollars for things you don't even need, especially those ridiculously expensive sneakers, and that's after tax dollars. I have nothing against sports, but none of the players or team owners need your money as much as you do. The same goes for those trendy tattoos and high priced concert tickets that come with costs for parking, food, drinks, hotels all adding up to many more hours out of your life necessary to earn the money to pay for it. All this for a few hours of so called pleasure along with a good deal of stress. It's definitely not an investment that will support you when you want to stop working. In the alternative you can often enjoy the same events for free on the Internet or T.V. in the relaxed environment of your home, alone or with friends. Remember these examples the next time 'a once in a life time, can't miss thing' comes along. Save those for when your investments pay for them instead of you having to work for the money. Then, if you want, get that tattoo, get one that says 'I did it!' And for those of you who spend much of your time and money following your entertainment and sports heroes, remember the words of Steve Jobs, 'Your time is limited, so don't waste it living someone else's life.'

I will remind you too of that aspect of wealth previously mentioned, and that is, to always appreciate what you have. If you can't appreciate what you have enough will never be enough. Tom Shadyac a prolific and successful Hollywood director, author of one of the books on your recommended reading list entitled, *Life's operating Manual* and writer/director of the film called *I Am,* traveled the world in search of what gives meaning to life. While in India, he met a man who lived in a slum along with his wife and many children. Their home was a shanty made of discarded wood and sheet metal with no running water, electricity or plumbing. During the day the man worked long hours pulling a pedicab transporting people throughout the city with his legs and feet. A night he came home to his family exhausted, but as seen in the film he told Tom he felt grateful for all that he had, to a point of being moved to tears. Hard as he worked pulling that pedi-cab every day, he felt blessed that important people chose him to transport them to their destinations; blessed too, that he had a home while others lived on the street; blessed that he had a caring wife and children to come home to; blessed that they had enough to eat while others did not. On the flip side I have known people who have vast material wealth and live in large homes in exclusive, expensive neighborhoods with all the privileges and comforts money can buy yet are not wealthy in spirit because they are always wanting more and often fixated on what they don't have and the problems associated with accumulating and maintaining material abundance. They can't eat, they can't sleep, and they can't enjoy their life for want of more and/or the fear of losing what they have. I have a friend who accumulated over twenty million dollars and that was a decade ago when it was worth a lot more than today. He once said to me 'I don't know what's wrong with me, all my friends have considerably more money than I have.' Hopefully, sharing these thoughts will help you maintain perspective and make better choices going forward.

Don't forget your reading assignments for next week and the journal assignment on *Compulsions and Desires*. Where they come from, how they manipulate your life experience and how they keep you from changing your life for the better. Have a great week, I look forward to seeing you then. Class dismissed."

CLASS THREE

THOUGHTS ON POWER

Professor Meyer: "Good afternoon. Today we are going to talk about Power, but not in the sense you may be accustomed to understanding the word. As used in this Course, Power is not the ability to impose your will on others, but something much more challenging and rewarding, the power to change your life. There's a saying in Buddhism that goes: 'What you think, you become.' Meaning that your life experience is shaped by your thoughts. In other words, a primary reason people don't achieve the life they want is they don't adopt those thoughts that can lead them to that goal. If we can get hold of the thinking process, we can actually remake ourselves. Destructive ways of thinking can be rechanneled and constructive ways of thinking can be deepened by changing the way we think.

So a little later today we are going to explore two methods by which we can break free from our conditioned thoughts by gradually changing our habits through exercises that are easy to incorporate into our daily life. These exercises are central to attaining the power to change your life.

There is a famous book, over one hundred million copies sold, by author Napoleon Hill called *Think and Grow Rich* which purports to chronicle the combined wisdom gleaned from more than five hundred of America's most successful individuals of the era including Henry Ford and Andrew Carnegie two of the richest men at that time. The ideologies leading to success as outlined in the book are, 'to place yourself within the overall scheme of creation; obeying natural laws that inevitably and invariably beget growth, expansion and renewal; something called generativity, the propensity and willingness to engage in acts that promote the wellbeing of younger generations as a way of ensuring the long-term survival of the species; and the psychological power of thought and the brain in the process of furthering your career for both monetary and personal satisfaction, meaning your mind can either stop you or propel you toward becoming the best version of yourself, and once you set your mind to do something, the only thing remaining is to take action with enough consistency to achieve the goal. In summary, the three elements to achieving the life you want are one, an appropriate mindset; two, an appropriate corresponding action, both of which are under your control; and three, fate which is not under your control and therefore should never be of concern.

While the title implies all you have to do is change your mindset, the text reminds us that we must also engage in the appropriate action and that's where problem often occurs. A lack of conviction leads to deferment. It's one thing to know what to do and it's another to get it done.

Over the years people have come to my office seeking assistance saying they had innovative inventions and ideas believing them to be their eureka pathway to great financial reward. But when I would ask them what that invention or idea was, they would not tell me out of fear it might be appropriated. While some of that concern is valid, I would remind them that the real value of any invention or idea is in its execution. Inventions and ideas are a dime a dozen, even very good ones, it's the ability to implement them that turns them into dollars.

The distinguishing characteristic of people who achieve empowerment is they are self-disciplined and have worked hard to cultivate the habits that produce results. They may not earn the most. They may not be the smartest. They just have developed good habits by practicing them consistently over long periods of time, and small changes consistently practiced over long periods of time lead to empowerment. Another way of saying this is good habits lead to the action that produces the result; it is simple cause and effect. Right habits are the simplest way to cross the bridge between the life you have and the life you want. You don't have to intellectualize the process or overcome massive obstacles. You don't have to get ready to get ready. What Napoleon Hill discovered is expressed in the saying 'Your belief is as deep as your action.'

Perhaps now would be a good time to pause and talk about your journal exercise for this week on the subject of compulsive behavior that negatively affects your life. Who wants to begin?"

Student: "The first five lines included in the exercise description got me thinking about something I never thought about before: 'watch your thoughts they become words; watch your words they become actions; watch your actions they become habits; watch your habits they become character; watch your character it becomes your destiny.' I learned that a conditioned habit becomes a compulsion and a permanent part of our personality through repetition. I struggle each and every day with trying to understand and control my habits. Trying to differentiate who I am inherently versus who I am as a product of my conditioning; the nature vs. nurture debate. It's difficult to determine which came first, the action or the conditioning. At least that is how I felt up until this journal exercise. How much of my personality, my being am I in control of? I suppose that is why books such as *The Purpose Driven Life, Man's Search for Meaning* and other such books by persons who have experienced significant trials and tribulations have intrigued me. All address the issue of individual control over ones actions and reactions. In essence as you have said, although we may not be able to influence the actions of those around us, we do have control over how we react to a situation at hand."

Professor Meyer: "Exactly. We can't control what comes into our lives, but we can control how we respond to it and that's what gives us the power to change our lives. Who's next?"

Student: "To paraphrase Eknath Easwaran we think of ourselves as consistently the same, but we are actually remaking ourselves every moment by what we think, say and do. 'Just as our bodies are in a constant state of repair and change, the cells that made up our bodies are constantly dying and new sells are replacing them, so the old cliché *I'm not who I used to be*, is right on. I recently came across the quote, 'Isn't it funny how day by day nothing changes, yet when we look back everything is different.'

It is comforting to know that undoing a habit is possible even if it is the most challenging battle a human can face. I have found that so many of my behavior habits are more like reactions than actions and have been detrimental to the situations. The easiest example I can give is my attempt at improving my eating habits. Before reaching for an unhealthy snack I now attempt to think about what I'm doing and the potential consequences both long and short term. As you and our text books suggest regarding changing compulsive behavior, instead of telling ourselves no, we should tell ourselves yes, but to wait a few minutes before acting on it. The idea is that the compulsion or craving will diminish or dissipate during that time, because a new one will come to mind. So when I have a strong desire to just give into it I just have to wait a few minutes before doing so. Changing habits is difficult, it's a constant, never ending battle that requires awareness, action, time and emotional strength."

Professor Meyer: "Thank you for sharing that. Who wants to go next?"

Student: "A few years ago I became ill and began to exhibit negative and self-destructive behavior. After receiving proper medical attention I was asked to develop some methods for dealing with stress and my negative habits and behaviors. Writing in a journal using colored pencils to fill in a coloring book, taking walks, creating origami, and reading were all methods that I used to try and distract me from my initial urges and instead focus my attention elsewhere. It has been some time since I have had to use these coping methods, but I think they would provide a wonderful means for trying to help conquer my other habits. As Professor said, 'when you can shift your attention away from a habit, the habit is immediately weakened a little and the will to resist is strengthened.' Both my coloring books, reading books, origami paper and my journal are next to my bed and I think it is about time that I start using them again."

Professor Meyer: "Thank you for sharing that. Who's next?"

Student: "I have a difficult time admitting it, but I have some extremely self-destructive habits. I think if I can develop a method to attack them I will not only have the self-confidence, but the means for addressing the more significant ones and improving myself by changing my behavior and my attitude toward situations that present themselves to me."

Professor Meyer: "Thank you. Next."

Student: "Every day I have compulsions. What I find most often is that I get impatient. Impatient while driving usually leads to anger. I also find myself getting frustrated when teaching someone a skill that I find mundane. For example when teaching my dad how to use his new phone, I got very impatient and then angry. After reading this journal exercise I tried to catch myself when those feelings arose. Normally they just run their course but the other day I tried to do the opposite of the emotion I was feeling. While driving in traffic I became impatient, but then realized the traffic situation was out of my control and began to relax. With others it was not so easy. When I became angry with someone in a group project it was very hard to turn that anger around into a positive. What I did realize however is being aware of these thoughts allowed me to catch myself before I acted and that was beneficial. I will continue to practice this and be aware of my thoughts and emotions as they occur."

Professor Meyer: "Thank you for sharing that. We will get into the process of transforming impatience and anger a little later on today. Who else?"

Student: "The conditioned behavior that I struggle with is being over analytical. I overanalyze things for days after they happen to try to understand what I did and stress out over what I could have done and what I could have done better."

Professor Meyer: "I think you will find that today's guest speaker will help you with that. Who else wants to share what they learned from doing this journal exercise?"

Student: "I completely yelled at my mother yesterday because there were some major complications outside my control and she started telling me that it was my fault and I need to learn to manage better. In response I told her to table the conversation because I was in a vulnerable place, but she didn't and I snapped. I just started saying how horrible I felt about myself and how I could not handle hearing it at the moment. I snapped emotionally in response to her over and over again. With everyone else I don't react this way, I stay calm, it doesn't get to me. But my pathway to emotion with her is engrained so deeply. I realize this is one area of my life I need to work on. I need to change the thoughts, words, actions and break the habit because this is part of my character. What if it became my destiny with other people I am close with in my life? That is not what I want."

Professor Meyer: "That was powerful. Thank you. Anybody else?"

Student: "One of my conditioned habits is being defensive when someone criticizes me. At work if someone criticizes me I usually internalize my defensive reaction because I do not want to seem argumentative. Unfortunately, I do not act the same way when my boyfriend gives me any type of critique. Although I know that he does not approach me out of anger, I do not react in the best manner. I usually become very aggravated and just begin defending my actions without really thinking. The way I see it, I have no other choice than to react defensively. This is something

I really need to work on because every time I do sit and think about what he is saying to me I realize he is right. Unfortunately, it takes me some time to come to this realization and this only happens after we have already been fighting. I need to just calm down and not let my emotions rule my actions. This is much more challenging than it sounds. I have tried this many times and for some reason, when I am in the heat of the moment I cannot calm myself down. I think the secret is constantly remaining conscious of my actions. I do not want to overreact and be defensive when someone approaches me with something I may not want to hear. People are not going to compromise themselves to please me all the time. And although I realize this, I have yet to take the next step and gain control over myself."

Student: "I'll go next. For me it is reacting negatively to what my girlfriend says or does or doesn't do. Over the years I think I've become good at not letting things get to me and not turning molehills into mountains. But in thinking about this journal exercise I realized I was able to convince myself that this was a part of my personally that I could disconnect from, change and re-channel the wasted energy into something else."

Professor Meyer: "Thank you both. Who else?"

Student: "The conditioned behavior I am trying to work on is being more patient with my girlfriend. I consider myself a very patient person when it comes to most things, but for some reason sometimes I lose my patience when I am dealing with my girlfriend. Usually I'll have a snide comment for her when my patience is tested and I feel bad about making the comments almost immediately after the words leave my mouth."

Student: "I'll go next Professor. The conditioned behavior that negatively affects my life is my habit of procrastination. This is an area that has plagued me for as long as I can remember and although I always make sure to get everything that is necessary done, without exception I always wait until the last possible second to do so. I believe my problem with procrastination stems from my thoughts about the things I need to get done. I realize the things in my life that are very important to me I always have time to complete, but things that I enjoy less fall to the bottom of my to do list. At first I thought that this was a good thing, that I was prioritizing my life well, but after more introspection I realized that this was not so."

Professor Meyer: "Thank you both. Next?"

Student: "I'll go next. I have battled against anger most of my life. Until this assignment I never thought of anger as a conditioned habit but an unfortunate personality trait that a person is born with, but after reading the journal assignment and the text assignment it made sense that if a person conditions himself to constantly react in the same way, then it becomes part of their personality and it also becomes very hard to change."

Professor Meyer: "Thank you. Next."

Student: "Two of the most common conditioned behaviors I have are fear and doubt. I have become fearful of almost everything like getting into an accident and this has creeped into every aspect of my life. I've become a germphobic out of fear for diseases and deal with everything through a worst case scenario state of mind. The same with doubt. I suffer from doubting my ability to achieve and this has crept into every aspect of my life such as academia and business success, even my intelligence and appearance."

Professor Meyer: "It seems all of you have a lot to say on this subject. Two more then we have to move on."

Student: "This exercise was very interesting because it made me much more aware of the emotions that I embody. I was actually quite surprised at how many little things affected the way I feel. I always thought I was laid back, but as I looked further into my feelings and emotions. I began to see that it wasn't that I never get upset, but rather I tend to keep my emotions on the inside. For example, when my boyfriend upsets me or does something that would normally make me angry, rather than get upset, I play it off, but on the inside I'm allowing anger to take over my thoughts."

Professor Meyer: "Thank you. And the last one."

Student: "When I started this week's assignment, I began to realize that my life and wellbeing have been plagued by negative conditioning for years. Chief among these are impatience and bad temper. Because I have been naturally gifted with a keen intellect, I often become frustrated when people around me are unable to grasp concepts quickly. As such, my typical response includes noticeable agitation and cynicism. This compulsion was put to a test this weekend with my girlfriend who is academically smart but often slow in areas of common sense. We had dinner reservations and show tickets, but as always she ran late. I have a stereotypical bad temper and quickly unleashed my anger. Most of my fury is targeted toward trivial matters. I look forward to hearing about practices of reversing my negative behavior."

Professor Meyer: "Thank all of you for sharing your reflections and insights. Now let's move on and explore ways in which you can acquire the power to change compulsive behavior into choices; the power to transform anger into affection and compassion, impatience into patience and to stop worrying and make the best of your life experience regardless of what it brings to you. Integral to the process of transformation is the capacity to develop detachment and discrimination in dealing with habitual impulses; two abilities you need in order to make beneficial choices. Many of you are likely pre-dispositioned to contextualize these words in the negative such as detaching yourself from your feelings and discriminating against people and things you don't like or don't want. But as used here they are very much positive. Detachment means detaching yourself from your ego by denying its demands so you are free to make decisions that will benefit your life experience rather than be detrimental to it. For example, your ego may tempt you to engage in unethical or immoral behavior whereas the ability to detach yourself from such impulses will clear the way for you to make better choices. After gaining mastery over your ego one of the things you will discover is that you receive a good deal more joy from not getting what you want than getting what you want, because it changes compulsive behavior into free chose and addictive behavior into preferences; you become the master of your ego rather than its slave. As Easwaran tells us, 'without detachment we are compelled to do what the ego wants no matter the cost; this causes us to try and manipulate others to satisfy our demands instead of to do what is best for all concerned.' It makes us believe we can always get what we want when the truth is regardless of how it appears nobody wins all the time; all of us win some and loose some along the journey of life. Furthermore, the more we indulge the ego the stronger and more demanding it gets and the weaker our ability to resist it. That is why seemingly powerful people make foolish, self-destructive decisions.

As for discrimination, 'it is the ability to perceive and respond to differences among choices and is considered a more advanced form of learning than generalization. Further, it is the capacity to see where our choices will lead us; without which we cannot make wise choices.' Two quotes attributed to the widely acclaimed sage Albert Einstein expound on this, 'The definition of insanity is doing the same thing over and over again and expecting a different result' and 'Education is not the learning of facts, but training of the mind to think.'

One point I want to make before introducing you to one of the tools for attaining self-empowerment is, that power cannot be sustained when it is confined to the self, it must be deployed to serve the welfare of all; it's what nourishes and feeds our soul. As Meister Eckhart the German theologian wrote, 'Nature seeks and hunts and tries to ferret out the track in which God may be found.' And Easwaran, 'The whole purpose of every experience, every activity, every faculty, is to turn the human being inward and lead him back to his divine source. And from savant investor Warren Buffett, 'I know people who have a lot of money and they get testimonial dinners and they get hospital wings named after them. But the truth is that nobody in the world loves them. If you get to my age in life and nobody thinks well of you, I don't care how big your bank account is, your life is a disaster.'

If suffering exists it is not possible for real power to be sustained unless it is used to alleviate this suffering. There's a story that comes to mind. Some years ago while on a business trip to the country of Haiti, one of the poorest countries in the world, a guide took me to see the ruins of what was one of the most opulent resorts in the world, built to attract the rich and famous. As the story goes, the developers decided to route the entry to the resort from the airport through the poorest slums in Port-au-Prince, the Country's capitol city, to enhance by contrast, the magnificence of the resort. Only the plan had the reverse affect by producing such guilt, shame and disgust in those who viewed the slums that the resort failed shortly after it opened. The story illustrates that while we may try to shield our conscience from the suffering of others by living in a bubble world, we inherently know that we cannot experience peace as long as suffering exists. The sole purpose of power is to alleviate suffering; if we misuse this power we will never know peace. And, if we want our children to grow up to be happy and secure we need to teach by example. As Mahatma Gandhi said, 'make of yourself the world as you want it to be.' Telling them one thing and doing something else just won't work.

Now it's time for me to share with you the first of two fundamental tools for transformation and empowerment. I'll start by positing this question. If you came to me with a headache and I said I could take your headache away in two seconds, what would you think?"

Student: "It doesn't sound possible."

Professor Meyer: "What do you think would happen to your headache if I stomped on your foot real hard with the heel of my shoe?

Student: "I would no longer be aware of my headache, because my foot would hurt more?"

Professor Meyer: "Exactly. I am not suggesting this as a cure, but using it to illustrate that the mind can only entertain one dominating awareness at a time. Most of us have likely heard of multitasking, but some researchers don't believe it is possible; that a multi-tasking mind is more likely jumping from one dominate thought to another rather than simultaneously experiencing multiple thoughts. Assuming this is so, along with the adage, 'change your thoughts, change your destiny' what it tell us is, if we exchange one thought for another thought we can alter our behavior in a way that will change our destiny.

Here's an example of how the power to change your thoughts can be used. If you are worried and I told you to stop worrying what would you say?"

Student: "If only it was possible."

Professor Meyer: "By a show of hands who would like the ability to stop worrying?"

All hands go up.

Professor Meyer: "Would it surprise you to learn that worrying is a conditioned habit that has become so ingrain through repetition it appears to be a necessary part of our personality; one that we have no control over?"

Several *yes* responses from the students.

Professor Meyer: "The fact is we absolutely have the power to stop worrying. Would you like to know how?"

More *yes* responses from the students.

Professor Meyer: "What we think of as our personality is really a collection of habits that have become rigid compulsions and when we are compelled to act it means we are not free to choose how we behave. Eknath Easwaran says 'Until we are free from our compulsions we are like puppets and our compulsions are the puppeteers. Responding to anger with anger and impatience with impatience are two examples of this. And each time we respond this way we are strengthening and perpetuating the compulsion.

But just as compulsions are formed through the process of repetition, that is repeating the same response to the same stimuli, we can recondition them through the process of changing our responses. For example, when a compulsion comes up, respond to it by doing something different than what you have done. If you feel angry force yourself to respond with kindness even if it means faking it many times over until the feeling becomes real. Each time you do you weaken the compulsion and are being kinder to yourself and the recipient of your anger. The same process applies to any habitual or compulsive behavior be it impatience, smoking, over eating or worrying. When those compulsions come up simply train yourself through a process, starting with small changes in how you respond, by doing the opposite. Each time you do you are one step closer to changing your habits and one step closer to being free to choose the responses that will be beneficial rather than destructive.'

Culturally we have been conditioned to believe we can solve problems by worrying about them or at least lessen the consequence of a problem by worrying about them. The conditioned belief being if you worry about the outcome and the outcome is unfavorable it will somehow buffer the suffering by preparing you for the worse. In my experience prolonged dwelling on a problem is counter-productive on all fronts. There is a wise saying, and you know how I like wise sayings, that 'worry is interest paid on a debt than never comes due' and another that says 'worry never robs tomorrow of its sorrow, it only saps today of its joy.' Eswaran analogizes worry to sitting in your car with the transmission in neutral and the engine running, you burn vital energy without going anywhere. I have found if you dwell on a problem and no solution comes to mind after a few moments it is best to move on, meaning drop all thoughts of it and get busy with something else or nothing at all. And when you do, the solution will unfailingly present itself sometime later, seemingly out of the blue. Noted physicist Albert Einstein reportedly said, 'I think 99 times and find nothing. I stop thinking, swim in silence and the truth comes to me.' If you can do something about a problem do it, but if you can't, don't continue to dwell on it.

The first tool you can use to gain power over your thoughts and relinquish their control over you is called a mantra. Who has heard of a mantra and can tell us what it is?"

Student: "Is it like yoga?"

Student: "Or meditation?"

Student: "Is it a chant you repeat to calm your mind?"

Professor Meyer: "Yes. Remember when I said that the mind can only grasp one thought at a time? Well, repeating the word or words of a mantra replaces the thought you don't want with the word or words of the mantra. The word *mantra* can be broken down into two parts: 'man' meaning mind, and 'tra' meaning transport or vehicle. In other words a mantra is a word or phrase that is repeated in the mind for the purpose of keeping your attention focused on it, versus the thought you want to replace. To be clear there are many different opinions on mantras and how to use them, but all of them have the same end goal, that is to keep the mind from wondering and in the process transform your consciousness. Some teachers of mantra advocate repeating the mantra out loud as in chanting, others advocate repeating the mantra in silence. Some of you may sense a similarity of purpose with certain religious practices such as the use of so called prayer beads, aka worry beads in Greek and eastern religions, and Rosary beads in the Catholic tradition, but they involve a physical component whereas mantra intentionally bypasses the physical and goes straight to the source of the problem which is centered in the mind. I want to remind you going forward that any use of the word 'god' in connection with mantra in this class is in a spiritual sense, you are free to associate it or not within a particular religious or secular context as the case may be. In any event mantra will lead you to the same place. Additionally, for the purpose of this class exercise I am advocating that you keep your mantra to yourself and repeat it in silence. For one, it will allow you to practice in public without garnering unwanted attention and for another, it will become something very personal like an alter ego that you won't want to share with anyone else.

In choosing your mantra trust your intuition. Easwaran advocates choosing a mantra from your spiritual tradition for example, 'if you come from a Jewish tradition you might choose 'Barukh attah Adonai' which means 'god is great.' If you come from a Christian tradition you might chose the name 'Jesus or Hail Mary.' If you are Muslim the name 'Allah or Allahu akbar.' If you are agnostic or atheist you might chose something that resonates with you in a very personal way, perhaps just the word 'calm' or 'peace' or 'peace be with me.' You can read his *Mantra Handbook* listed in your Course materials under recommended reading for more help and guidance in choosing your mantra.

Once you have chosen your mantra practice it for a few days and if doesn't resonate with you, you may choose another, but do not go on changing it more than once or twice because to be most affective you have to keep the same mantra for the rest of your life otherwise as Eswaran says in his handbook, 'it will not go deep enough to effect the change in your consciousness that will give you control over your thoughts and emotions.'

Like mastering any skill in life, be it a musical instrument, a sport or a martial art, to be effective you must practice it every day throughout the day at every opportunity for the rest of your life. Every time your mind wonders onto something you do not want to dwell on like worry, impatience, depression, anger or compulsive eating, repeat your mantra silently in your mind. At first this will be challenging because the compulsive thoughts will be fighting for your attention, but with repetition and practice you will become proficient and advance through stages analogists to martial arts beginning with your white, yellow and orange belts, then advancing on to your brown and black belts and at each level you will achieve greater mastery over both the process and your thoughts.

The science behind mantra is sound; that compulsive thoughts do not have any power over you in and of themselves, but derive their power from the attention you give them and when you withdraw this attention they disappear. Thus your mantra can help you transform impatience into patience, make worry disappear, dissolve anger, conquer fear, greed and depression, change bad habits into beneficial ones, improve personal relationships, vanquish boredom, keep you focused on your goals and live life in the present. Whenever you are angry, feel irritated, afraid, nervous, worried, resentful, impatient, tempted by greed, smoking, or unhealthy eating all you have to do is repeat your mantra until those thoughts and the emotional energy driving them dissolve into the mantra itself.

The mantra will give you the ability to calm your mind so you can make decisions unclouded by emotions, cultural conditioning, judgments and misunderstandings and over all help you lead a better life.

To aid you in getting started I have prepared an envelope, one for each of you, that contains two items, a four inch long wooden dowel and a sheet of instructions on how to choose and use a mantra. The symbolism of the dowel comes from Easwaran who grew up in south west tropical India where elephants were used to do heavy lifting like carrying logs for the construction of buildings. As he tells it, the elephant's trunk is restless, always in motion, swinging back and forth looking for something to grasp onto and he uses this as a metaphor for our mind that is always restless and always searching for a random thought to grab on to. Further, when the elephant passes by a roadside vendor selling bananas or coconuts its trunk reaches over and grabs a bunch of bananas or a coconut just as our mind grabs on to this thought or that. To solve this problem the mahout, who is the driver that sits atop the elephant, gives the elephant a stick to hold on to with its trunk thus preventing the elephant from grabbing anything else. That stick and the dowel in your envelope is analogist to the mantra which prevents the mind from grabbing on to another thought. Carry that dowel wherever you go to serve as a reminder to use your mantra throughout the day whenever your attention is not needed elsewhere such as when standing in line waiting, or walking or doing mechanical chores and just before you fall asleep at night. If you do, you will find that the mantra will help keep you relaxed and alert during the day and help you sleep during the night.

The mantra will also keep you from dwelling on the past. Whenever a thought arises over something in the past just simply repeat the mantra. To quote Einstein again, 'Time does not exist – we invented it. Time is what the clock says. The distinction between the past, present and future is only a stubbornly persistent illusion.' All our attention is best focused in the present where every moment is fresh; every relationship is fresh; every decision available to create your experience.'

The mantra will also allow you to forgive a transgression and move on. When we withdraw our attention from a perceived wrong it is not possible to be resentful. There is also no possibility of staleness or boredom in your life when you live in the present because every moment is a new opportunity.

In summary the choice is simple, be a slave to compulsive thoughts or be the master of your mind. So let's begin now. Take a few minutes to select a word or short phrase to use as your mantra; chose anything that comes to mind, but it should be meaningful on a personal level and peaceful and positive. Let me know when you are ready."

After a few minutes.

Professor Meyer: "Are you ready?

From the students: "Yes."

Professor Meyer: "While the Mantra can be used with your eyes open or closed, for the purpose of this practice close your eyes and slowly repeat your mantra silently to yourself until I tell you to stop. Don't anticipate when this will be or concern yourself with me or those around you, just slowly repeat your mantra and don't worry if your mind wonders; if it does just gently bring your attention back to your mantra."

Five minutes later.

Professor Meyer: "Okay, you can stop now. How was your experience?"

Student: "I was very surprised. On one hand it was amazing in that I did not think of anything when I was repeating my mantra. On the other it was very difficult to keep focused on the mantra as other thoughts kept popping up."

Professor Meyer: "That's not unusual. Your ego, your sense of self, has had free rein most if not all of your life and is not going to cede territory without a fight. As I previously said in comparing it to martial arts, you are not going to go from a white belt to a black belt in one day. Who else?"

Student: "I had a similar experience it was difficult to keep my mind focused on my mantra, but as other thoughts came into my mind I did what you said and kept pulling the mantra back and in doing so I can see how it could really work. I'm excited about the possibility of gaining control over my thoughts."

Professor Meyer: "Congratulations, you have taken the first step of reclaiming that space. Many religious texts describe what you have experienced as a battle between your ego thoughts and silencing your mind so that you can know god in a spiritual context, or if you prefer in a secular one, meaning uniting with your essential nature. The Bible instructs us to, 'be still, and know that I am God' and in this silence you will find wisdom, and it goes on to say 'even a fool who keeps silent is considered wise' and again from Albert Einstein, 'when you examine the lives of the most influential people who have ever walked among us, you discover one thread that winds through them all. They have been aligned first with their spiritual nature and only then with their physical selves' and 'The true value of a human being can be found in the degree to which he has attained liberation from the self.'

It's a battle between the temptations of the intellect which binds us to the phenomenal world and separates us from our spiritual nature, and our innate desire to return to our primal origin like the salmon that swim upstream to get back home. And it's also the battle described in the Bible between David and Goliath; David representing the spiritual world and the giant Goliath who represents the physical world. And again in the allegory of Adam and Eve where the Garden of Eden represents our spiritual home and the tree of knowledge the phenomenal or physical world. You might recall the first thing Adam and Eve experienced after leaving Eden was their nakedness which symbolizes their transition from experiential unity to that of the physical awareness. The message being we have to live with one foot firmly rooted in the spiritual world and the other in the phenomenal world. This is what mantra helps us to do. I ask that you not to take my word for this, but to experiment with Mantra in your own life and decide for yourselves. If your life experience is better with Mantra I assume you will continue, if not, than you won't. There is no need to over intellectualize this because it doesn't matter; what matters is, does it make your life experience better or not. And the only way you will know is to practice it in earnest for an appropriate period time, then reflect on the results.

In the interest of time, by a show of hands, how many of you had a similar experience with Mantra to those who already spoke?"

All hands go up.

Professor Meyer: "Okay. Then let's take a ten minute break. When you come back our guest speaker will introduce you to another discipline that will help you gain mastery over your life. Be sure to return on time. If you are late you will have to wait out in the hall so as not to interfere with the speaker's presentation."

Following the break.

Professor Meyer: "Our guest speaker today is Dr. Sabrina Strauss a tenured professor of religious life at the University of Central Arizona, a visiting professor at the University of Massachusetts Center for Mindfulness and a researcher at the University of Southern California Meditation Awareness Center.

Prior to these positions Dr. Strauss spent six years studying and teaching at the Center for Mindfulness Meditation of the University of Mumbai, Mumbai India. To date she has published six books on Meditation and Mindfulness and has been featured in several magazines including *Forbes* and *Time* and has appeared on a number of TV programs including *60 Minutes* and *CBS Sunday Morning* as a lead-ing authority on Mindfulness Meditation. She's here to-day not only to address us on this subject, but to guide us through the experience. Please welcome Dr. Sabrina Strauss."

Following the applause.

Dr. Strauss: "Thank you for welcoming me here today. I appreciate the opportunity to pass on to you what I consider the most important practice a person can undertake to improve their lives and the lives of others.

I recently returned from New York City where I stayed in *The Benjamin Hotel.* Its central location in mid-town Manhattan makes it ideal for both tourists and business travelers. I was pleased to find listed in their welcoming package that they now offer *'On Demand Meditation'* in recognition of just how important meditation is to their guests' wellbeing.

You may have heard the expression 'All that we are is the result of what we have thought.' But I would modify it to read, 'All that we are is the result of what we have thought and not thought.' because when we clear our mind of thought we experience the unity of our nature versus the chaos of our day to day lives and it is this unity that we need to replenish ourselves and solve the problems that plague our physical existence. To many it never occurs to them there's more to life than our physical self and the sensations we experience. Or that our thoughts think us rather than us thinking them. Yet there's a unifying existence that goes beyond the physical/intellectual universe. It connects each of us to one other whether we are aware of it or not. John Dunne's famous poem *For Whom the Bell Tolls* addressed this other universe when he wrote "*No man is an island, Entire of itself. Each is a piece of the continent, a part of the main.* Meaning we are all connected to one another and our environment and we all must rely on this connection in order to thrive. Great problem solvers know that once they have gathered all the facts they must set them aside and connect with this unity to solve the problem. Meditation is a means through which we are able to experience this connection.

The problem with trying to solve problems solely through thinking is that the process takes place on the surface level of life where we are driven by conditioned self-centered beliefs that sometimes cause us to seek personal gratification without regard to its consequences. That leaves us open to manipulating others for our own gain and conversely being manipulated by others as they seek their own personal gain. We end up running toward that which we like and away from that which we do not like while trying in vain to avoid the inevitability of what goes up must come down. When our likes and dislikes collide with those of others we experience disharmony yet are not willing to make the necessary changes that will produce harmony, balance and fulfillment. Through meditation we discover there is a better choice.

I know that Professor Meyer has introduce you to the writing of Eknath Easwaran who explains the different states of awareness, like waking, dream sleep and dreamless sleep all of which are levels of reality. Easwaran writes, 'in dream sleep our consciousness is withdrawn from the body and the senses and there's only the mind which is not necessarily a restful state as any of us who have experienced nightmares can attest to. In dreamless sleep our consciousness is withdrawn not only from the body and senses but the mind too. In this state our ego has dissolved and our self-will extinguished along with our physical desires and fears. In its place is a higher state of knowing called the unitive state.

Instead of knowing through our minds we know through the experience itself. It's a reconditioning process that allows us to appreciate what ever life brings to us and we recognize that everything is an opportunity to move us closer to our true nature and the simple realization that what pleases us pleases others, not on the surface, but deep down where we are connected through this unity.' This is what Henry David Thoreau discovered when he immersed himself in nature at Walden Pond. 'I went to the woods' he explained, 'because I wished to live deliberately, to front only the essential facts of life, and see if I could not learn what it had to teach, and not when I came to die, discover that I had not lived.' And what Albert Einstein, your professor and I both like his quotes, discovered when he wrote 'I think 99 times and find nothing. I stop thinking, swim in silence, and the truth comes to me.'

If you look up meditation on Wikipedia, it defines it as a practice 'in which an individual uses a technique – such as mindfulness, or focusing the mind on a particular object, thought, or activity – to train attention and awareness and achieve a mentally clear and emotionally calm and stable state.' Meditation is practiced in numerous religious traditions. Christians, Jews and Muslims may refer to it as "interior prayer". But I like the narrative that says prayer is when you talk to god and meditation is when god talks to you.

Meditation connects you to your spiritual self and gives you a greater sense of peace, calm and balance because you are not conflicted by societal conditioning. This benefits your emotional well-being and overall health even when you are not meditating. Studies show it also lowers your blood pressure, reduces pain, and boosts your immune system and brain function. It induces a decidedly different state of awareness that helps you act instead of react to the situations in your life and promotes critical thinking through detachment to the conditioned responses. I believe your professor has talked with you about detachment and its importance in wellbeing.

There are many types of meditation. There's mindfulness meditation where you focus on what you are sensing and feeling in the moment whether it be your breath, guided imagery or your thoughts as they pass through your mind without lingering on them; a process often analogized to the trail a bird leaves as it flies through the air.

Then there's focused meditation where you concentrate on external objects like prayer beads, a candle flame, a sound, or a photo.

And Mantra meditation where you concentrate your focus on repetition of your mantra be it a single word or phrase or an inspirational passage, silently repeating it in your mind.

And visualization meditation where you focus your attention on feelings of peace and calmness by visualizing positive scenes, images or persons while embodying their qualities.

Today I going to guide you through a mindfulness meditation. Before we begin, how many of you have meditated in one form or another?"

A few hands go up.

Dr. Strauss: "What was the experience like?" "

Student: "Professor Meyer just guided us through a mantra meditation.

Dr. Strauss: "What was that like?"

Student: "It was difficult to stay in that space. Various thoughts kept breaking my concentration"

Student: "I meditated on a candle flame once?

Dr. Sabrina Strauss: "Tell us about that experience."

Student: "It felt like I was in a hypnotic state."

Student: "I mediated on a running stream on a camping trip and got so calm I fell asleep."

Dr. Strauss: "All of those experiences are not unusual even for some who have been practicing meditation for years. What's important to remember is when you practice meditation you always receive its benefits despite those issues and with practice the benefits increase while the distractions decrease.

Are you ready to try a mindfulness meditation for five minutes?"

All hands go up.

Dr. Strauss: "Sit upright in your chairs, shake out any tensions in your bodies. As you do, notice how your arms feel, how your legs feel and how your body feels. Then close your eyes and take a couple of slow deep breaths, fill your lungs with air and slowly exhale to a count of five. Focus your attention on your breath as it enters then exists your nostrils. Continue to slowly inhale and exhale giving your full attention to each breath. Repeat this silently for the next five minutes letting everything external disappear from your awareness along with any concern about time or place; concentrate only on your breath. I brought a small metal cymbal with me that I will use to signal the end of the session with a single chime so don't think about time all at. And remember, if your mind wonders don't fight it, just gently bring your attention back to your breath.

Five minutes later Dr. Strauss strikes the cymbal.

Dr. Strauss: "How was it? Who wants to tell me what they experienced?"

Student: "I had a hard time staying focused, but did not want to stop; I was so relaxed.

Student: "I also had a hard time staying focused on my breath. I kept wondering if the people around me were also experiencing the same thing."

Student: "I really felt calm and relaxed."

Student: "It felt like I could drift off and float away at any moment."

Student: "At first it worked and everything around me disappeared, but then I heard some noises and it brought me back into the classroom and I couldn't get back into that space."

Dr. Strauss: "All those experiences are not unusual especially during the early stages of mindfulness meditation because consciously changing the way you breathe sends a signal to the nervous system that it has not experienced before. Would you like to try it again, this time for a ten minutes?"

Most of the student's hands go up.

Dr. Strauss: "If some of you would rather not, feel free to abstain. To those who are ready, let's begin. Shake out any tension in your bodies noticing how your arms feel and your legs feel and your body feels. Take a long, slow deep breath in and focus on the point where your breath enters your nose. Hold it for a moment then slowly exhale while focusing on the point where your breath exits your nose. If your attention wonders gently guide it back. Don't concentrate on any distraction because that will direct your attention away from your breath."

Ten minutes later Dr. Strauss strikes the cymbal.

Dr. Strauss: "Was that any better? How did it compare to your previous experience?"

Student: "Yes, I had less awareness of my body and my surroundings."

Student: "Me too. I forgot where I was."

Student: "I felt completely at peace."

Student: "I kept going in and out of concentration, but it was easier to get back to concentrating on my breath."

Student: "I wanted to keep going."

Dr. Strauss: "Gaining proficiency in meditation takes consistent practice. It's best to set aside two or three minutes each and every morning to practice your meditation than to plan on meditating for a longer period of time once or twice a week. Because no matter how busy your schedule might be you can always find two or three minutes and it will establish the habit of meditating as consistency is the key to success in this discipline. Just make it a priority and get up early each morning to make sure you have the time to meditate. When I'm on a business trip with a five AM flight to catch I just get up that much earlier to make sure I have time to meditate and I've never missed a day in more than twenty years. If this seems daunting, how many of you would think of leaving your house each morning without brushing your teeth? Nobody can say they can't find two or three minutes first thing in the day no matter how busy they are. Once it becomes an ingrained habit you can increase the time perhaps to five minutes. And once that becomes a habit you can increase the time again toward an ultimate goal of half an hour, but not much longer or you might run the risk of it running up against other commitments that might ultimately cause you to skip it now and then and eventually put it off altogether. With regards to habits, one of the benefits you will experience when you meditate daily is that harmful habits such as unhealthy eating, smoking, drug use, impatience, anger, will give you up rather than you having to give them up."

Student: "Dr. Strauss, can you please explain what you mean by habits giving us up rather than us having to give them up?"

Dr. Strauss: "Yes of course. When the mind is racing with thoughts coming and going throughout the day like cars racing around the track at the Indianapolis 500, you have little control over them; try making a turn at a hundred miles per hour. But when you slow the mind down in meditation you connect with the unifying source that is always in balance and it drives out that which is at odds with this balance. You have likely experienced this when hiking in the stillness of a forest, or gazing across the magnificent vastness of plains or valleys, or in the stillness of the desert where the loudest sound you hear is the buzzing of a bee half a mile away. Nature heals the soul and habits that don't fit in slowly fade away. Are there any other questions?"

Student: "I'm intrigued by what you say about this balance, can you elaborate on it a little bit more?"

Dr. Strauss: "The force behind unhealthy habits is an innate sense of disharmony or imbalance; something is just not right. So we seek to achieve balance thorough physical acts, trying to fill the void with physical things like food or drugs or even excessive exercise. But when we achieve balance through meditation the disharmony is gone and when you habitually reach for that cigarette or extra cocktail or extra helping of food the craving is gone; you may not know why, but it's simply not there."

Student: "Do you ever get sick?"

Dr. Strauss: "A good question. Thank you for asking that. Rarely and when I do it has always been mild with symptoms lasting only a day or two. Before I meditated on a daily basis I use to get a prolonged cold at least once a year. Since then I haven't gotten a single cold in decades. Nor have I experienced any depression or worry or significant lack of energy. I get up every day inspired by the moment and what might lay ahead."

Student: "You make it sound too good to be true."

Dr. Strauss: "I'm glad you made that observation, because my goal in coming here is to inspire you to explore these experiences for yourselves."

Student: "Have you ever encountered someone who couldn't meditate or had a bad experience with it?"

Dr. Strauss: "The short answer is no. Some have had more of a challenge maintaining the focus or the consistency, but

I've never encountered anyone who had a bad experience. Changing long held habitual behavior takes motivation and inertia and the stronger your motivation the better your chance of success."

Student: "I'm curious, are you married and if so does your husband meditate? And if not, how has meditation affected your relationship?"

Dr. Strauss: "Another great question. Yes, I am married and my husband does meditate, but that was not always the case. Marriage is the ideal circumstance for meditation. In marriage we often have a relationship based not on who the other person is, but who we envision that person to be or who we want them to be. For the relationship to thrive we have to be willing to go against ego driven desires for self-centered gratification and put the other person's happiness before our own. In order to do this you must be in that place where separation does not exist, where we see the other as an extension of ourselves. What makes him or her happy makes us happy."

Professor Meyer: "Unfortunately we are running out of time. One more question before we have to let Dr. Strauss go and vacate the classroom for the next group."

Student: "Dr. Strauss, how can we use meditation in business?"

Dr. Strauss: "Meditation is the ideal antidote for stress, anxiety and worry. It also builds real confidence versus the

Dennis Torres

fake kind and you know intuitively you can handle any challenges life sends your way. In addition, it is the ultimate problem solver because you become more respectful of others which fosters an environment of trust and mutual benefit that's synergistic in creating solutions."

Professor Meyer: "Thank you Dr. Strauss for your excellent presentation. Let's show Dr. Strauss our appreciation."

Following an exuberant round of applause Dr. Strauss leaves.

Professor Meyer: "To summarize today's class I offer these closing remarks. Easwaran reminds us that 'through the practice of mediation we find the freedom in which we are able to give our very best without being caught up in others reactions and others attitudes. Even if they are irritable we can be more generous and we find that everyone around us benefits from our freedom. They will lower their defenses and will gradually give their very best without any worry or fear because while everyone has different dimensions there is a common core in all of us.'

He goes on to say, 'Most of us identify ourselves with our opinions. Then, when we are contradicted, we take it personally and get upset. If we could look at ourselves with some detachment we would see how absurd this is. There is scarcely any more connection between you and your opinions than there is between you and your car, and once we realize this at a deeper level of consciousness, most of the resentment in differences of opinion disappears' This

142

kind of detachment does not come easily, but it can be cultivated. Why not try sitting back from your opinions with a little detachment. After all it doesn't mean you have to give up your opinions. You don't have to agree. The real issue is not opinions at all; it is how to lower the barrier of self-will that keeps us from relating freely to everyone. You can understand another's point of view without having to agree with it. But when you understand it, it enables you to listen with real interest, because it helps you to understand your own position better as well. What prevents us from doing this is the lack of detachment; we don't know how to disagree with complete respect.'

The power to change your life is facilitated through the use of Mantra and Meditation because they help you to de-condition then recondition your conditioning. Conditioning is created through the process of repetition and causes us to respond the same way to the same stimuli. Once we are grounded in the experiential awareness of unity we can begin the process of reconditioning. So when a situation presents itself don't act on it in the same way, hesitate for a few moments to sever the tie with your conditioning then begin the deconditioning process by deliberately responding in different way. For example if you would have responded with impatience deliberately respond with patience. If you would have responded with anger, deliberately respond with kindness. And if you would have responded by taking that second helping of food or drink deliberately walk away. Soon you go from the concerted de-conditioning process to being newly reconditioned and that's how you gain the power to change your life. Another of my favorite quotes, this one attributed to Gandhi is 'As human beings our greatness lies not so much in being able to remake the world – that is the myth of the atomic age – but being able remake ourselves.'

Are there any questions?"

Hearing none Professor Meyer continues.

Professor Meyer: "I can confirm through my own experience the benefits of meditation that Dr. Strauss and Eknath Easwaran talk about. I grew up being overweight. Besides over indulging, a good deal of being overweight to the point of compromising your health and wellbeing, has to do with being conditioned to a poor chose of foods. When you meditate besides poor habits eventually giving themselves up, you also become intuitively aware of what you eat and soon lose your taste for things that are not good for you, such as foods that are not easily assimilated by the body perhaps because they are processed to a point of not being food at all but a product manufactured for profit and they stick around in your body with no place to go. I once picked up a single serving of a popular yogurt in the supermarket and notice it had the circled "K" on it meaning it was certified as kosher. But when I looked at the ingredients rennet was listed. Rennet is a complex set of enzymes produced in the stomachs of ruminant mammals and I knew that mixing dairy with meat was not kosher according to Jewish law and therefor the product could not be kosher. So I called the company and asked them how this could be. They told me that the product was certified kosher by a well-respected rabbi. When I contacted the rabbi and asked him the same question he told me that after processing the rennet it no longer bore any relationship to a cow. While I did not agree with his conclusion it's an example of how the processed food industry manipulates natural ingredients to a point where they bear no relationship to natural food. It is my sense that healthy eating consists of a plant based diet as close to their natural unadulterated form as reasonable notwithstanding that the human body can often adapt to a variety of diets that seem to contravene this belief.

As Dr. Strauss said, it is through meditation our desire for things that are unnatural and unhealthy slowly disappears and we find ourselves shedding harmful habits in favor of more beneficial ones. The speed of this process varies, but through consistent practice it steadily evolves and continues to do so throughout our lifetime. That's how my desires for cigarettes, recreational drugs, consuming animal flesh, slowly gave up on me and disappeared, and my emotions for anger and impatience continue to diminish to a point where they are rarely seen and when displayed are but a whisper of their former self. As Easwaran reminds us, 'whatever we think about most, whatever we labor for most, whatever we desire most, that is what will define our lives.

Student: "Professor if what you and Easwaran say is true why doesn't everybody meditate and why don't they teach meditation at every level of our education system?"

Professor Meyer: "From my observations, when the plague of self-indulgence infected all facets of our society with the disease of immediate gratification it obscured the desire for a cure. To paraphrase Easwaran, we became conditioned to prefer temporary satisfaction even if it meant permanent loss, to bearing a temporary displeasure that leads to permanent fulfillment; our nervous systems became habituated to one way traffic, away from what we dislike and towards that which we like and the antidote of meditation was not desired.

Before we leave for the day I want to talk to you about two more paths to empowerment. The first can be found in a book entitled *How to Give Your Kids $1Million Each, And it won't cost you a cent*, it's included in the Couse under recommended reading. A friend of mine who lives in Australia introduced me to this book. I was intrigued by the title and her experience in raising her children with it so she sent me a copy. After reading it I was convinced that its lessons should be taught by every parent and in every school. If fact if I were your age I would contact the author and work with him to turn it into an on-line Course for parents and children. The book does exactly what the tile says. It details how you can give each of your children one million dollars without it costing you one cent. But much more than that, it teaches your children about money, what it is, how to acquire it and how to manage it. All of which leads to economic empowerment, because its end goal is to provide your children with the power of choice as to how much of their lives they want to devote to working for money. And its formula works for any income level even those earning minimum and below minimum wage. I urge you to read the book and put its tenets into practice whether or not you have children and especially if you do.

The other path to empowerment is one I touched on earlier. It's based on how to become an essential person whether you are an employee or self-employed. Write down these three words and make them your credo in life. The words are 'consider it done.'

To become an essential person you must be the 'go-to person'. A 'go-to person' is the one who can be counted on to get the job done, in the time and manner it needs to be done, without further involvement by the person needing it to be done; in other words, that person can 'consider it done.' I mean no disrespect to any of you, but based on my experience most of you are not likely to be that person, but I sincerely hope you prove me wrong.

There are lots of good, smart, capable people who can get the job done, but very few who can be counted on to get it done, on time and in the manner it is supposed to be done without troubling the client or boss. When those few people say 'consider it done' the client or boss never has to give it a second thought and it frees them to deal with all the other things on their plate. The 'consider it done' person is also proactive and finds out what needs to be done, then gets it done. By way of example, if you work for an organization like GRU that depends on donors to cover a percent of its operation, even if you are the maintenance person you can find donors and if you are successful in doing so you will be the last person to get laid off and the first person to be considered for a promotion and/or raise. From my experience, the average employee only considers the work called for in their job description and only at the level expected of them and nothing beyond that. The 'go-to, consider it done' person is always seeking to go beyond that which is expected of them. Are there any questions?"

Student: "Professor Meyer, why do you say only a few of us will be that person?"

Professor Meyer: "As I stated, it was not intended to insult or demean anyone in any way, but simply reflects my experience that many people only seek to do that which is expected of them and nothing more. It reminds me of that old joke about a job seeker being interviewed for a job who asks the interviewer 'how much will I get paid' and when the interviewer replies 'we will pay you however much you are worth', and the job seeker replies, 'I was paid more than that at my last job.' Many people are procrastinators or lack the determination or creative thinking to go beyond the task at hand in implementing its execution. They don't see the difference between good enough and excellence, or a minute here or a minute there, even when it doesn't matter, as long as the task gets done and I can tell by how, to some of you, getting to class on time, or getting your papers in on time, or putting in the effort to go above and beyond in completing an assignment, doesn't matter as long as you get it done or as long as you get a good grade. Yes, you might get that good grade, but you have conditioned yourself not to be a 'go-to person'."

Hearing no response Professor Meyer continues.

Professor Meyer: "As a reminder, your Assignments for next week include practicing your Mantra and Meditation and being prepared to discuss your journal assignment entitled 'Preference vs. Additions. Instructions for these can be found on the Course website. I look forward to seeing you next week and continuing our conversations on how to acquire, wealth, power, success morally and ethically. Enjoy your week. Class dismissed.

CLASS FOUR

THOUGHTS ON SUCCESS

Professor Meyer: "Good afternoon welcome to Class four entitled Thoughts on Success. Question, when you envision success what does it look like to you?"

Student: "Being happy."

Student: "Having accomplished something worthwhile with my life."

Student: "Having a family, a nice home, a profitable business."

Professor Meyer: "Those are good definitions along with the most common one, that of attaining great wealth and eminence. Note that those definitions are central to the mind and subjective. I would like you to consider yet another, experiencing the state of fulfillment. Many Greek philosophers including Plato, Socrates and Aristotle considered success as the primary purpose of life defining it as being satisfied and contented with one's life just as it is.

I once read a story about the original founders of McDonalds restaurant, two brothers named Richard and Maurice McDonald and Ray Kroc who purchased the business from them for 2.7 million dollars; a million dollars each plus $700,000 to pay the taxes on the two million. As we know, Ray Kroc ultimately turned it into a multibillion dollar industry. Depending on who you believe, Kroc had a handshake deal with the brothers to pay them in addition to the 2.7 million dollars, half a percent of the gross profits from the business. As the story goes Kroc allegedly reneged on that promise cheating them out of a lot of money. Whether the story is true or not I don't know, but a person who claimed he knew the brother's very well said that while the brothers had issues with Kroc they never let it ruin their happiness in life. That 2.7 million in today's dollars was worth more than eight million dollars when they received it and the brothers felt blessed by this success.

Contrast this story with that of Leonard Shoen, the founder of U-Haul who transferred all but two percent control of the very successful Company to his children which eventually led to family squabbling and lawsuits pitting siblings against siblings, children against their father and father against his children. And even though Leonard prevailed in the lawsuits he committed suicide. There are many, many similar stories of so called successful people involved in intra family disputes. Another that comes to mind is the Haft family of the Dart Group that pitted wife and son against husband and father. It too was very tragic; you might want to research it later.

Admittedly there are a lot of nuisances, half-truths and mistruths in these stories, but I use them to illustrate something I have personally encountered many times in my life, particularly in my career as a mediator and arbitrator of litigated cases, where otherwise successful people due to their compulsive obsession to have their way were unable to enjoy their so called success. This brings me back to my opening question of what does success look like to you and its segue into this week's journal assignment on Preferences vs Addictions as defined by Ken Keyes, Jr. in his book *Handbook to Higher Consciousness* which is on your recommended reading list. That definition is as follows:

'An addiction is a conditioning of your emotional bio computer that causes you to manipulate the world around you into fitting your addictions. Addictions cause you to respond with anger, worry, anxiety, jealousy fear etc. whenever the world around you does not give you what you want.

A preference on the other hand, is when you choose to do something without the addiction to do it. You are happy to do it, but you are not dependent on it for your happiness; you are not trapped by it.

When a preference is not satisfied, you are simply indifferent, after all it's only a preference, but when it is satisfied it adds to the texture and beauty of your life.

Only your emotional programing determines whether something is an addiction or a preference in your life.'

Who wants to share what they learned in writing this assignment?"

Student: "That not all preferences are choices. There is an element of stimulus and conditioned response which in the assignment is called an addiction. We think we are choosing to do something, but it turns out we are conditioned to respond in a certain habitual way."

Student: "An addiction as used in our journal assignment is behavior that is compulsive to a point of eliminating the element of choice."

Student: "We think we are freely choosing, but are being manipulated by our conditioning."

Student: "If you are addicted to something you have lost the ability to control your behavior."

Professor Meyer: "Now contrast the definition of addition with how the term 'preference' is defined in the journal exercise?"

Student: "A preference is something you chose to do, but if it turns out you aren't able to do it, it doesn't affect your mood or happiness."

Professor Meyer: "Give us a personal example from your Journal paper."

Student: "My girlfriend preferred that we go see the movie *The Twilight Saga* and I preferred we go to see *Transformers*. We ended up going to *The Twilight Saga*. Admittedly I was bummed out, even a bit angry for having been coerced into going. Which according to the definition used in the Journal assignment meant my wanting my way and being bummed out about not getting it, was an addiction not a preference. Because if it was a preference I would have gone to her choice of movie, not be bummed out and still had a good time; which I didn't."

Professor Meyer: "Thank you for your candor. Who else?"

Student: "When I started doing this assignment I didn't agree with the definition of addiction which I always thought of as being addicted to drugs and alcohol. But then when I reflected on my feelings when I don't get my way, I realized how similar my reactions were to those of addicts when they don't get their alcohol or drugs."

Professor Meyer: "Can you give us an example."

Student: "I dated a wonderful girl for almost a year. She liked Thai food and I preferred Mexican food. We compromised and sometimes went to Thai restaurants and other times to Mexican restaurants and we both learned to enjoy each other's preferences and always had a good time. But she was from Chicago and I'm from LA and I just couldn't get over the fact that she was a *Bulls* fan and I'm a diehard *Lakers* fan so we broke up. I could never be with a girl even as friends who was not a *Lakers* fan."

Professor Meyer: "Thank you for those examples of a preference versus an addiction. Anybody else?"

Student: "My boyfriend is addicted to stupid video games and I hate them. He's a great guy but I question whether I could ever marry somebody who prefers video games to being with me."

Student: "Doing this journal exercise I never realized how addicted I was. I always considered myself a flexible, go with the flow, easy going person. But that was on the surface. While I realize I do always go along with others I also realized how bummed out inside I am."

Professor Meyer: "Some of you may still wonder what this journal exercise has to do with the subject of today's class. In order to be successful you will need to understand the difference between choice and compulsion so that your compulsions don't interfere with your emotional wellbeing which is a key measure of success under my suggested definition of experiencing fulfillment. Wants are subjective and you are not alone in the world which means nobody gets their way all the time. So how you react when you don't get your way and how you react when you do, will determine whether your life experience will be a success or failure. You can have all the material wealth in the world, and all the love in the world, but if you can't realize them you will not be a success under this definition.

As previously said, I have known many highly successful people in terms of accomplishments, but their compulsive obsession with getting their way drove them to a life of misery. All they could focus on, to the exclusion of family, friends, material comforts and day to day blessings, was getting their way and this left them emotionally and physically ill. One of these was a very wealthy Beverly Hills couple who were divorcing after fifty plus years of marriage and their divorce case went all the way up to the high court because they ran up millions of dollars in attorney fees owned to multiple law firms and refused to pay claiming the lawyers failed to settle the divorce. In finding for the lawyers, the court noted that the all the attorneys involved tried to settle the divorce many times, but the clients refused to settle unless they got their way. If the wife wanted a certain tea cup the husband would tell his lawyers he didn't care how much it cost he would not give it to her and vice versa. In the end the High Court ordered the couple to pay the Lawyers' fees in addition to nearly half a million dollars in back interest. The couple then tried to get the Supreme Court to take the case contending that their civil rights were violated because it shouldn't cost millions of dollars to get a divorce."

Student: "What happened?"

Professor Meyer: "The Supreme Court wouldn't take the case. Now in furtherance of our discussion on addictive behavior in particular how it is conditioned, I'm going to introduce you to one of the greatest salesman of all times. A man who took a relatively worthless product and got you and most everyone else in the industrialized world acculturated into accepting it as a symbol of success. Not only do you feel you have no choice but to buy it, but the company he founded tells you how much you should pay for it. I'll give you a hint, it's expensive even for the very rich. Do any of you want to try and guess who this super salesman is or what his product is?"

Student: "Bill Gates, Microsoft software?"

Student: "Steve Jobs, Apple products?"

Professor Meyer: "Neither of them. For one thing their products are utilitarian and the product in question has virtually no utilitarian value. In fact it is almost worthless outside the demand he and his company, created for it. I'll give you another hint, the man's initials are C.R. Any guesses?"

Hearing none Professor Meyer continued.

Professor Meyer: "The man's name is Cecil Rhodes. Does anyone know who Cecil Rhodes is?"

No hands go up.

Professor Meyer: "Have you heard of the Rhodes Scholarship?"

All hands go up.

Professor Meyer: "Have you heard of the Country of Rhodesia, now known as Zimbabwe in Africa? It was named

157

after Cecil Rhodes. When I tell you the name of his company many of you will recognize it and all of you will likely know the product it sells. The company is De Beers. Who can tell us what De Beers is famous for?"

Student: "Diamonds!"

Professor Meyer: "Yes and contrary to common belief diamonds are not that rare, gold is significantly rarer. Nor do they have much of an intrinsic or dollar value, even for industrial use. Nor are they with some exceptions, a good investment; a diamond is a depreciating asset since it loses a large portion of its value the moment you buy it. There's a famous quote from a former De Beers chairman Nicky Oppenheimer, 'diamonds are intrinsically worthless.' Essentially, the value they have is attributed to their perceived value and this perception was intentionally cultivated by De Beers. All this making what Ceil Rhodes and his company accomplished in creating a worldwide desire for diamonds one of the most successful marketing campaigns ever in terms of a tangible product; a product that has become a must for couples wanting to marry. Prior to De Beers sapphires and rubies were the most popular gems for engagement rings.

How did Rhodes and De Beers do it? Initially they gained control of the rough diamond supply by buying up the mines and limiting the rate at which diamonds were mined; essentially controlling the market through a monopoly. The tactics and means they used to gain control allegedly included murder and kidnapping.

The Company maintained a monopolistic hold over the diamond market by controlling 75-85% of the rough diamond supply and released only enough to satisfy market demand while continually adjusting the degree of rough diamond availability. By creating demand and controlling supply they essentially controlled the prices making them escalate and at the same time reinforcing the perception that diamonds are rare and in short supply. In today's market they even tell you how much you have to spend on an engagement ring. Can anybody tell me what that is?"

Student: "The equivalent of three months' income."

Professor Meyer: "Yes, can you believe the audacity and even more that we the public, buy into it without protest. If you doubt this, how many women in this room would require a diamond ring before accepting an engagement to marry?"

Almost every female student's hand goes up.

Professor Meyer: "Even after hearing me tell you how manipulated you are and that diamonds are a bad investment, you still have to have one?"

Student: "Yes, it's custom and tradition and I don't care if they are really worth the money or not."

Professor Meyer: "Do you see what I mean? Even those of you from countries outside the United States have been conditioned to believe you have to have that diamond. And not only that, you and your boyfriend are going to be judged by your friends and family by the size of the diamond and how much it cost. That's why I say Cecil Rhodes was one of the greatest salesman the world has ever known."

Student: "Professor, my desire for diamonds is definitely one society has conditioned in me. I was brought up in a very wealthy neighborhood where most of the people had competition about their wealth and what they were able to buy, not only for themselves, but for their loved ones. It was a daily thing where people compared what they bought, how much it cost, and what kind of new fashion they had."

Student: "For me it's all about cars and technology. I like expensive cars and Apple technology, but my girlfriend/ fiancé will be the biggest financial challenge in my life. I feel an obligation to entertain her, spend money on her, and provide a life for her with many of the material comforts that I know she enjoys. I hope to share the books and concepts taught in this class with her so that we can be on the same page financially."

Student: "So much of what manipulates me is based on the things I need to do or acquire in order for the people I associate with to approve of me. Or at least that is what I have been brought up to believe. There's a sense that all that matters is that others perceive us as successful and what is less important is if we're living up to our more fulfilling goals and dreams. We are manipulated into doing things so that others think of us highly, on a totally flawed system of judgement, instead of doing the things that fulfill us and will endure."

Student: "I've gotten caught up in this too, where I've worried about the clothes I wear, the car I drive, the job I have and how successful I appear to others. Some of the things I obsess about have now taken on a life of their own and it's hard for me to trace how or why they have become so important or how I became manipulated by them in the first place."

Student: "During my undergraduate college I found myself in a city where every kid my age including my classmates drove luxury vehicles and wore Tiffany necklaces and Dolce and Gabbana sunglasses. This was the norm and almost everyone else seemed to have them except me. As a result, I began to desire a flashy career where I could make enough money to have these same things."

Student: "Me too. I had the same experience and post-graduation I began a career in marketing for a fast paced youth-trend driven company. Its brand was based on keeping up with a rare, edgy style and living like a celebrity. Ironically, I was a marketer who became the ideal customer. Commercials and marketing companies were telling the world that in order to be happy, we needed to live like celebrities. We needed to wear labels and have things that seemingly no one else had. We had to have rare, expensive sneakers. We had to have jeans with Swarovski crystals on them. We had to drive Bentleys and be surrounded by other people who are doing it. I bought into the hype and equated my own happiness to the celebrity lifestyle. But when I looked at my bank statements and credit card bills and net worth after a couple of years, I realized that what I had thought was happiness was actually a short-lived rush that eventually ended in a sort of sorrow. And those people I was surrounded by were actually what the authors of *The Millionaire Next Door,* called 'big hat, no cattle.' My relationships were suffering and all I had was stuff. So I realized that real happiness came from an inner satisfaction with myself and my life, not continuing to live a fake millionaire life. As a result, I now focus my life not on desire for material things, but on being satisfied and finding peace with the person I am and the people in my life."

Student: "Most of the material things I buy or want to buy are a direct result of what I see on television being perceived as desirable. Sometimes when I am purchasing an item I say to myself 'okay this is the last thing I will get for a certain period of time.' Most of the time this doesn't work and I find myself wanting a new item even faster than I would have before. All this to say how powerful advertising is and in the context of what we are discussing how Cecil Rhodes and De Beers managed to condition all of us to need, his product."

Student: "The story of Cecil Rhodes and De Beers is emblematic of how media influences society and how they virtually manipulate our desires to get what we think we need, mostly to the detriment of our goals in life. Nearly everything we do has to do with trying to satisfy desires that have been programed into us to benefit the programmer. Why do we buy overpriced jeans, why do we get angry if our love interest doesn't get us the right card or gift on Valentines' Day or Mother's Day or Christmas Day or our Birthday or get to go on that trip of a lifetime or watch the Super Bowl or go to the Rolling Stones' Concert or the hottest new restaurant or the shoes or car or body piercing or tattoos. Why are we carrying water bottles when all previous generations have lived perfectly well without them?"

Student: "As Professor Meyer has said, the very nature of desire is that it is insatiable. The allure of satisfaction has more to do with future promises than present experience and we will spend our lives chasing it but never finding it and if we do find it, it won't be long before we need to find it elsewhere. Our personal relationships are a most telling and tragic example of this. We are programed by society that happiness can only be had by possessing something or controlling someone. Happiness will never be ours if we keep looking outside ourselves to satisfy our desires. The truth, as pointed out in our text books for this Course, is that the less desires we have, the happier we will be, the richer more joyful our life experience will be, the less conflict we will have because others will not be able to manipulate us and we will have no need to manipulate them."

Professor Meyer: "Very well said, I'm impressed. Who else?"

Student: "I can see where society creates perceived needs for the consumer. I like to listen to music so I have created a need for an IPod to listen to all my songs. Another perceived need was for a Facebook page that I have to interact with at least twenty times a day to the detriment of meeting with actual friends."

Student: "I have made the mistake in the past to buy stuff I didn't need and this was mainly due to an external source telling me that I needed it. However, these experiences have had a lasting influence on me. Every time this happened I realized my mistake shortly thereafter when I saw that the item's personal use to me was not worth the price, then judging myself for buying it and promising myself to be more thoughtful the next time and never do it again. These experiences helped me to evaluate what I really need and what is actually worth its money for me. Nevertheless, it happens occasionally that I catch myself buying useless stuff again. Two weeks ago I bought a small eight dollar toy figurine classified as art that I thought I really needed. I realized soon after that I did not need it and became dissatisfied with myself. The figurine stands on my desk now to remind me to think twice the next time I 'intuitively' want to buy something."
Student: "This discussion made me realize how manipulated by society I am to desire a career for financial success. During this Course I have realized how unimportant that desire is. I've realized that what is important is to have work that is satisfying emotionally in a way that makes me feel as if I'm contributing to the world in a beneficial and unique fashion. I'm glad that I took this Course to set me in the right direction since business school can sometime set me on a course that is not aligned with the teachings we've explored in the Course."

Student: "Taking this Class opened my eyes to how unimportant possessions are. Logically, I know that possessions cannot make you happy because there is always something new to crave and desire. I went through years of being upset and sad that I was not born into a family with money. I thought it was unfair that I didn't have parents who could work and give me everything that I saw other children having. I still have the desire to have fashionably trendy clothes, shoes, and jewelry but I think that the strength of that desire is dying down, especially after having taken this class."

Student: "Thanks to this Course I disposed of my television much like Professor Meyer did when he was my age. I think television, along with social media, are two of the greatest vehicles though which large companies can program us to believe we need or want certain material things in order to be satisfied. Within thirty minutes of watching television the food commercials make me so hungry for their food even if I don't particularly like it and would normally never consider putting it into my body. Half the time commercials are subconsciously dictating our desires. The same goes for magazines. As Professor Meyer pointed out magazines are mostly advertising interspersed with a few stories. This class has taught me to think critically about my desires and ask myself if I really need something or simply being influenced to buy it."

Student: "I truly am a minimalist and am much happier when I have the least amount of things to take up my time and worry about. For example, during college I went on a sort of binge where I decided to build up my DVD collection and I was continually buying new DVDs, whether I truly wanted them is another story. Then, after about three months I had buyer's remorse for all the DVDs I had purchased and had not watched more than once. In addition, it bothered me that they were taking up so much space in my room and where not useful to me at all."

Student: "One desire that I have filled consistently is entertainment. Every week I meet up with one of my good friends and we see a movie together. I did not question this before, it seemed like a good way for us to catch up with each other. However, after thinking about desires and their origins, this activity seems to be almost defeating the whole purpose of why we get together in the first place. We previously thought that by seeing a movie together every week we would fulfill our needs of friendship, but instead we are actually zoning out for one and half to two hours not speaking with each other or interacting whatsoever. The time before or after is spent eating and conversing, but the movie, which costs around eight dollars each time seems to be a complete waste when examined in this new context.

So where did this come from? Our society has taught us that it's perfectly normal and even entertaining to see movies with friends and loved ones. In fact, when asking what a typical first date is many people will answer dinner and a movie. What's interesting is that while dinner may reveal personality through conversation, the movie basically acts as a time waster. What could someone possibly learn about someone else on a first date while watching a movie and essentially ignoring the other person? Yet somehow I feel it would be difficult to convince others of this."

Professor Meyer: "Wow that was an inspiring exchange of ideas, but we have to move on. Thank all of you for those personal insights. Achieving our goals to be successful requires the ability to think critically about what we need to make us happy. Without this we are vulnerable to the manipulation of others. Let's continue to explore the meaning of success in the context of how it applies to each of us personally by using another one of the classic definitions as a starting point: 'The criteria for success depends on context and may be relative to a particular observer or belief system.'

You might recall from our previous class, in response to some of you telling me you want to get rich I suggested in terms of monetary resources you are likely in the top one percent of the world's population yet are still dissatisfied and wanting more."

Student: "Yes I was one of those, but how can I feel rich if I have money struggles every day?"

Professor Meyer: "Do you think it may be because you see your glass half empty instead of half full? Do you remember what our guest speaker Mr. Ahmadi said about living frugally and appreciating what you have instead of what you don't have? And what I said about how you can't control what comes into your life, but you can control how you respond to it?"

Student: "I get your point, but it hard to find balance in my life, which is one of my criterion for feeling successful, when the imbalance is caused by my money struggles."

Professor Meyer: "That may be because you don't see struggle as an integral part of success, like a stepping stone contained within success itself."

Student: "Can you elaborate on that?"

Professor Meyer: "Think of it this way. Success is as much a journey as an end in itself; a process and a state of being at the same time. Collective wisdom tells us that the end result of our actions is not within our control. The Bible echoes this with the passage 'man plans and god laughs.' And Buddhist wisdom with, 'you can control your action but not the end result of it.' And Albert Einstein when he said, 'The most important decision we make is whether we believe we live in a friendly or hostile universe. I believe in a friendly universe. Being receptive and allowing things to happen is a skill that can be practiced. It helps to believe in a friendly universe—one that is supporting you at every turn so that you don't have to worry about the details.' And he also said, 'I didn't arrive at my understanding of the fundamental laws of the universe through my rational mind. But when my mind was not occupied with them.'"

Student: "So success is finding out what will make me happy, doing it and not worrying about what happens?"

Professor Meyer: "It's worth exploring. Give it time, work with a passion instead of an end goal, see how you feel, then decide if that path is right for you. There's a popular saying 'chose a job you like and you'll never have to work a day in your life.' Start off by asking yourself what you would do if money was not an issue? Then do it and see where the journey takes you. Some might think this impractical, but the element of survival is present in everything we do."

Student: "The problem is I don't know what I want to do."

Professor Meyer: "That's not unusual especially considering you've spent most of your life in school where your attention is focused on subject matter and not introspection. I would suggest you ask yourself what you have experienced so far in your life that you really enjoyed then do that and see how you feel. Don't be afraid of following your curiosity. When I was growing up my father was a salesman and frequently changed products, one year selling sewing machines, another insurance; another encyclopedias; another cars; another funeral plans etc. etc. He had so many business cards during his lifetime that I thought I could paper entire walls with them. With each change he felt he was going to strike it rich, this was going to be it. He never did and we lived rather modestly, sometimes solely on the income brought in by my mother's job. Not only that, I was embarrassed when people asked me what my father did because he changed companies so frequently versus my friends' fathers who had the same job with the same company or the same profession most if not all their life be it a factory worker, merchant, self-employed doctor, lawyer, carpenter or insurance broker. It troubled me too, because my friends knew what they were going to do after high school, either join the trade Union like their father or go to college and follow in their fathers' footsteps, and I had no idea what I wanted to do. I told my mother I like cars, which were a big thing when I was in high school, maybe I should become a mechanic. But in saying that I also knew I didn't have a natural gift for mechanics or the patience it takes when you turn a nut and it just won't come off like you want it to. My real passion was to become an explorer like those I read about in history class; men like Columbus, Cabot and Vespucci. But how do you get a job as an explorer? So my mom told me I had to go to college and after that I could do whatever I wanted. Not knowing what else to do I applied to one college the Fashion Institute of Technology (FIT) in New York City because both my sister and brother-in-law had graduated from there and when FIT accepted me I went there. It was the foremost college for those wanting careers in the garment industry from fashion design, to fashion merchandising to manufacturing. I enrolled in the manufacturing program and it was interesting, but I had no passion for it. Following graduation I got a very good job for a company headquartered on the seventy six floor of the empire state building. I can still remember being in that office and feeling the building swaying back and forth; I think half inch in each direction at the top. Anyway when they sent me to their factory in western Pennsylvania even though I was an executive, I said to myself I don't care if I owned the company and was making a million dollars a year

I don't want to spend my life in a factory. So I quit drove back home to New Jersey and got a job driving a big rig truck through a good friend whose godfather was high up in the Teamster Union. And I loved it! I was a free man, out on the open road with nobody to bother me and no work to take home at night and on weekends. Not only that, I was making more money than I was as an industrial engineer and more money than many lawyers and doctors. Several of my fellow drivers drove brand new Cadillacs which at that time were considered the top luxury car. Long story short, when it became routine and I felt I had learned all I could about the job I moved on. Looking back over the years I have had over sixty four different jobs and careers to date that I can remember, including being the explorer I always dreamed of being having explored remote areas of Latin America, the Amazon Rainforest and other countries of the world. I am certain I have forgotten a few jobs, but have written down those sixty four to share with you and will project them up on the screen in the hope they might inspire you to follow your passions. Ironically while writing them down it occurred to me I have followed in my father's footsteps just like my childhood friends did; although his multiple jobs were always in the same profession and mine weren't. I won't kid you, not all the jobs I had were fun. I had my share of ups and downs, but overall my life has been a great adventure and I have learned something valuable from each experience and am still learning. I realized too, that I no longer envy my friends who knew what they were going to do with their lives because they spent them in the confines of a factory or windowless examination room or office doing the same thing each day. I also learned there isn't anything wrong with staying with one job or profession, only it was not something for me.

Life goes by very quickly especially the older you get, because each moment going forward represents a smaller percentage of your life experience. For example, when you are born the next day equates to one hundred percent of your life experience and when you are thirty, forty or fifty years old that same twenty four hours represents a much smaller percentage of your life experience. Soon weeks pass like days, and months like weeks, and years like months until the end of the cycle comes. The importance of this is to constantly keep in mind that your life is finite and you only have so much time. You might want to write this sage quote down, 'you have all the time in the world, but not a moment to waste.' On the threshold of death you are not likely going to say, I wish I had spent more time at the office. Spend some time with family and friends and alone in nature. Just the other day I was in a restaurant that had dozens of photos of very famous people on its walls, world leaders, actors, noble prize winners, authors, singers and philosophers. People who were larger than life and I easily recognized most of them. It then crossed my mind the one thing they all had in common was, they were all gone; they had all died. It reminded me that I too will soon be gone leaving behind all treasures and concerns as will all of you. Some of you will not reach your fortieth birthday others not their fiftieth or sixtieth, it's not sad, it's only part of a natural cycle. So ask yourself what is really important in your life and what is not, than do what is important. Don't fall into the trap of putting off these important things until you reach a certain age or milestone. There is no such thing as tomorrow, there's only the moment and there's a time to work and a time to play; and when you work, work and when you play, play.

Go out and follow your passion and if you don't know what that is just choose something that interests you and go do it and if you find something that ignites your passion even more go do that. But don't flit like a butterfly without giving yourself a chance to learn from whatever you are doing and always be of service to others. There is a statement from the Hindu Bhagavad Gita that says, 'You have the right to work, but for the work's sake only. You have no right to the fruits of work. Desire for the fruits of work must never be your motive in working. Perform every action with your heart fixed on being of service to others and be even-tempered in success and failure.' The beauty of this wisdom is that it relieves you of the stress and worry about whether you will succeed and frees you to just enjoy what you are doing in the moment, because the future is not in our hands. Your life will work out just maybe not the way you expected it, but you will have likely made a comfortable living and had a fantastic journey. And importantly your zest for life, your passion, will inspire others to follow their passion.

My wife and I founded a charity of volunteer pilots who transport people with medical needs for free; many of these people fighting for their lives. On the organization's first anniversary we decided to have a celebration party and I telephoned several of the people we had helped throughout that year and invited them to the party. When they arrived, they thought they had been invited so they could thank all of us for helping them, but we told them they were invited as guests of honor so we could thank them for helping us to experience the joy that comes from helping others.

Along with your labors you must keep in mind a work/life balance: Take time for yourself, your friends and family. Exercise every day; eat healthy foods (garbage in garbage out); read, study, learn, limit entertainment (video games, movies, concerts, television) and instead do something for others, it will bless you in ways that will increase your zest for life. Get out in nature, let your mind drift in mindlessness fantasy and imagination.

A work/life balance is defined by one online dictionary as 'the state of equilibrium where a person equally prioritizes the demands of one's career and the demands of one's personal life.' Another dictionary emphasizes 'the minimization of work-related stress, and the establishing of a stable and sustainable way to work while maintaining health and general well-being.' And still another refers to 'the level of prioritization between personal and professional activities in an individual's life.'

Remember that none of you will escape problems and if you live long enough rich or poor you will have a lot of problems. I believe it was Oprah Winfrey who said 'the only difference between a rich persons problems and a poor person's problems are the number of zeros.' Before your life is over all of you will likely fall victim to crime, disease, lies, betrayal, injustice, tragedy and pain, they are only the flip side of good fortune. And no matter how pressing your problems are, it is more than likely as little Orphan Anne said, 'the sun will come out tomorrow.' So do something about your problems if and when you can, at times by seeking the advice of others who have more experience or wisdom, otherwise let them go, don't worry about them, do not stress over them. In my own experience I have discovered if I don't dwell on a problem the solution will come to me seemingly out of the blue when I'm in the shower or when my mind is occupied with something else or nothing at all; it has never failed, after all, every problem comes with its own solution.

Remember too, that anger and impatience are conditioned responses. As such they can be re-conditioned and completely reversed and eliminated. If you analyze anger it is simply that someone or something is not doing what you want them or it to do. Think about how ridiculous it is to expect another uniquely conditioned individual to do what you want them to do especially when you have difficulty getting yourself to do what you want to do such as giving up an undesirable habit for example. It's the same when the laws of physics or chance seemingly work against you and something breaks or you can't find something, or when you have a so called accident or something just doesn't go the way you want it to, these are normal occurrences in life. Objects will break, you will lose things and if you stand up you will likely fall at times. When you get angry you stress your mind and organs to the detriment of your own health; remember the saying, 'Anger is like taking poison and hoping the other person will die.' In your assignment about anger most of you said you do not consider yourself to be an angry person, yet in response to the question what makes you angry? Here's what many of you responded.

I lose it when someone:

Attacks me or someone I care about.

Talks down to me.

Uses me.

Oppresses others' rights.

Is stubborn without viable reason.

Thinks they know more than I do on subjects I know
    more about than they do.

Is selfish.

Disrespects the environment.

Drives slow in the fast lane.

Acts with sense of entitlement.

Attacks my family.

Attacks my religion or god.

Attacks my sports team.

Challenges my politics.

Teases me.

Is impatient.

Challenges my opinions.

Places their values, beliefs ideas on me (lays a trip on
    me.)

Falsely accuses me.

Tries to make me feel guilty.

Is stupid such as Telephone Company – customer ser-
    vice people.

Expresses illogical thoughts.

Disrespects the people and values I hold dear.

Treats me like a second class citizen.
Talks down to me.
Disrespects me.
Treats me in a condescending manner.
Exhibits disrespect.
Discriminates against me or other people.
Is prejudice.
Is arrogant.
Disregards my feelings.
Is greedy.
Is chauvinistic.
Is narrow minded.
Is intolerant.
Is unjust.

And that's the short list. Not bad for people who don't get angry or impatient! Practice your mantra and meditation to retrain your impulses in the same way you retrain other habitual behavior. Start with small steps of change. For example, when you feel yourself getting angry you might go for a walk while reciting your mantra until the anger subsides. Don't permit yourself to dwell on it, change your thoughts by reciting your mantra. Don't worry about making progress, change is a process, just keep doing the things you know will work to transform your anger and impatience into kindness and patience. In the beginning you may have to force the kindness and patience, but in this instance pretend can be a useful tool for change. Don't try to rationalize your anger and impatience either because that means you are dwelling on it. Are there any questions on this?"

Hearing none Professor Meyer moved on.

Professor Meyer: "What would you say is the opposite of success?"

Student: "Not being successful."

Student: "failure."

Student: "Being a looser."

Professor Meyer: "In asking the question I expected those responses, because many of us have been conditioned to think of success as positive and anything other than success as a negative. The big 'L' formed with your thumb and fore-finger against the forehead is a popular mocking sign for a looser. But isn't failure really just another aspect of success? The other side of the same coin? How would we know success without failure? There's a popular quote attributed to the prolific inventor Thomas Edison who along with his many inventions like the phonograph and motion picture cameras is credited with inventing the first commercially practical incandescent light bulb which changed the world because it made it possible to do many things at night that were previously only done during the day. While recounting the process of inventing it he reportedly said he had many so called failures, but they weren't really failures, because he learned hundreds of ways how NOT to invent the light bulb. In essence saying that failure is a stepping stone within success; simply an integral part of the process. You can't fall down if you don't stand up. So if your goal is to stand up, when you fall down consider you are that much closer to reaching your goal. The Bible puts it this way, 'indeed, the darkness shall not hide from you, but the night shines as the day; the darkness and the light are both alike to you.' And a Chinese proverb expresses it this way, 'It is better to light a candle than to curse the darkness.'

Life is a process meaning as new information presents itself there's opportunity to reevaluate the situation and in doing so find a new direction; even if that direction is abandonment of the original idea in which case the decision of abandonment should be considered a stepping stone forward as well. Process is filled with choices and in making them you should ask yourself will this choice bring me closer to my goal or further away from it. Are there any questions on this?

Hearing none Professor Meyer continued.

Professor Meyer: "Next, I would like to further explore with you again the two important disciplines previously mentioned that are vital to creating a successful life, detachment and discrimination. As Eknath Easwaren writes, 'detachment refers to being objective; able to separate yourself from the sensory temptations of self-will that drives you toward doing what you want despite the consequences and the interest of others. Detachment is a key factor in being able to break free from conditioning and its destructive habits like anger, abuse and impatience which overwhelm you and cloud your judgment when making important decisions. It is not indifference, but the ability to think critically and separate conditioned self-interest when making choices.

The first step in the process of developing detachment is to recognize the lack of it, then start by making small oppositional actions until you have reconditioned your impulses before moving on to larger oppositional actions and continue to do the same until you have become the master of these impulses rather than a slave to them. Avoiding these impulses will not work, you have to confront them, then continue to practice, practice, practice, and if you fall down, forgive yourself and go on. You can never stop practicing.'

Again, think of this process as you would a martial art. To master it you start with one skill and when you master that one you move on to greater challenges and master them. But you can never stop practicing, if you do, the skills you have mastered will be lost. Say for example you have a compulsion to over eat or eat things that are not beneficial to your wellbeing like those irresistible French fries that come with your 'happy meal'. Intellectually you know they're not good for you, cellulose sponges saturated with overheated fat and coated with excess sodium. Intellectually you don't want to eat them, but they are so delicious. So you tell yourself you'll just eat one – there's even a television commercial that says, 'I bet you can't eat just one' – then when your hand reaches for that second fry, you tell your hand 'absolutely not, I'm in charge here' and that very act is the most powerful thing you can do for yourself, because you have just struck a blow against the enemy, your ego, and strengthened you own army of self-will. The same goes for second helpings; never take a second helping no matter how hungry you are because you are in training to recondition your conditioned impulses which is much more important than the few extra mouthfuls.

Soon you will discover that you receive a good deal more joy from not getting what you want, than getting what you want, because you are changing your addictions into preferences. Always remember that your ego 'like a spoiled child has been conditioned to get what it wants no matter the cost to you and others. You are not the one making the decisions, but involuntarily reacting to life, trying desperately to manipulate life to satisfy your ego no matter the consequences; I want, I want, I want even if I get destroyed and destroy others in the process.' The more we indulge the ego the stronger and more demanding it gets causing us to try and manipulate life to get what we want instead of doing what is best for all concerned. Conversely the more we practice detachment the weaker the ego gets and the stronger we get. Are there any questions so far?"

Hearing none Professor Meyer continues.

Professor Meyer: "Detachment applies to our opinions too. Understand you are not your opinions, which are likely to change throughout your life, and they are not you. The same goes for the opinions of others. As Ken Keys, Jr says in his book *Taming Your Mind,* 'no one knows ALL about anything' and 'when we really understand the significance of the fact that we don't know ALL about anything, it is easy to acquire habits of open-mindedness.' Understanding this will hopefully lead us to the habit of critical thinking.

The success process means if you look only at the end goal you will get off track because when you learn something new it will take you to a previously undiscovered level. If you try to skip ahead you will miss the learning steps necessary to get to that next level. You only have control over what you are doing at the moment and not over the next step or the next or the end result. So don't concern yourself about them, just keep doing what is necessary to move you in the right direction. This frees you and your creative energies from being responsible for that which is out of your control so you need not waste time worrying and instead put that energy into the process itself. If you are attached to the result you will not enjoy what you do because you will be unhappy when things do not work out the way you want them to and perhaps more desperate when they do. I had a boyhood friend who was a compulsive gambler. Whenever he lost money he was depressed because he had not performed well and whenever he won money even a lot of money, he was depressed for not having had the courage to bet more. Are there any questions so far?"

Hearing none Professor Meyer continues.

Professor Meyer: "Discrimination on the other hand refers to your being able to recognize, then act in choosing what is beneficial to you and all concerned, over that which is not. Discrimination is what we need to make wise choices coupled with the capacity to see where those choices will lead us.

In order to do this you have to have a guiding philosophy, a core belief that you and everyone else are more than just bodies and minds. You have to have a deep innate awareness of the unity that connects each of us to one another and with the flora and fauna and the environment in which we exist Albert Einstein described our connection to this unity when he said, 'A human being is a part of the whole called by us universe, a part limited in time and space. He experiences himself, his thoughts and feeling as something separated from the rest, a kind of optical delusion of his consciousness. This delusion is a kind of prison for us, restricting us to our personal desires and to affection for a few persons nearest to us. Our task must be to free ourselves from this prison by widening our circle of compassion to embrace all living creatures and the whole of nature in its beauty.'

This awareness is necessary in order for us to live in humility and to forgive others for any transgressions and to forgive ourselves too. I think it was Saint Francis who is credited with saying that forgiveness is at the root of the Gospel, that it is the greatest gift of all, that only God is infallible. And that we cannot turn to God seeking his forgiveness for our transgressions and then turn around and refuse to forgive others for their transgressions against us. The Bible is filled with such sage advice, 'for as you forgive men their trespasses, your father who is in heaven will forgive you. But if you do not forgive men their trespasses, neither will your father forgive you your trespasses.' And the all too familiar prayer, 'Forgive us our trespasses as we forgive those who trespass against us.' Of course it can be very difficult to forgive those who have caused us great pain, but the alternative is to be consumed by hate, retribution and judgment. Remember the way out is to 'let go and let god'. I remind you again I use the word god in a spiritual sense meaning the essence that unites us all, but you may embrace it otherwise.

To illustrate the power of forgiveness I will share with you the story of a man named Peter Biehl who along with his wife forgave the killers of their daughter Amy age 26, a white Fulbright scholar who in 1993 worked in South Africa to improve the lives of the disadvantaged and was stoned and stabbed to death by four black men participating in a crowd shouting anti-white slogans. Following the conviction of these men, Peter Biehl and his wife lobbied the government for their release, then trained two of the men to carry on his daughter's work through the *Amy Biehl Foundation Trust* which has given millions of dollars to a variety of social programs and business projects in and around Cape Town. Nobel Peace Prize winner Bishop Desmond Tutu said of the Biehls', 'What was so remarkable was, not only that they forgave the killers of their daughter, but that they went so far as to rehabilitate them.'"

Student: "Professor while that's remarkable, I have to say if anyone killed my daughter I could never forgive them."

Student: "I feel the same way."

Student: "Me too."

Professor Meyer: "We've been conditioned to turn our hurt into anger and retribution which poisons us and those who comes in contact with us, and it does no good, that is why the Biehl's story is so remarkable and powerful. After Amy was killed, on the flight back to the U.S., Peter Biehl wrote his deceased daughter a letter promising to continue her work; he knew that's what she would have wanted and there's no better tribute to her."

Student: "I don't disagree, but I just don't think I have that in me to forgive at that level."

Professor Meyer: "No doubt that is true for many of us. The Biehl's story is to inspire us to make the changes within us through mantra and meditation that will help end the cycle of hate and judgment that is necessary to heal ourselves and others. That's what this Course is about, to inspire you to never to stop questioning and be curious enough to experiment with different ideas to see if they work for you in terms of improving your life experience, and to adopt them unless or until, something better comes along.

A few bullet point comments about success and a final statement before we take a break and come back to hear our guess speaker. Know your values. Spend time thinking about what is important to you in life. Practice time management. Set boundaries. Enjoy your work. Consider your finances. Nurture relationships. Focus on your health. Have down time. Manage stress. Manage change. Manage technology. Manage leisure time. And manage time for letting your imagination to drift freely.

Know, that when you are in a loving relationship you will very likely encounter problems with the other person. Don't let yourself become polarized by these, even if the other person is hurtful to you. Don't retaliate or give up on them. Instead move closer and give that person the support of your unconditional love; doing so will increase both of your capacities to love. If you run away from these relationship difficulties you will likely never know the joy of true love. Are there any questions?"

Hearing none, Professor Meyer continued.

"Okay, let's take a ten minute break and when you return we will hear from our guest speaker on his path to financial success. I think you will find it of interest in planning your own way.

Following the break.

Professor Meyer: "By way of background our guest speaker Bill Chambers is the founder and CEO of the Chambers Company, a highly successful investment banking enterprise. He also serves as Chairman of Chamber Securitas, Inc. a securities broker, Chairman and Managing Director of Chambers Capital Management Inc. an investment advisory group. A Former partner and chairman of the M&A department of Brown, Gable and Root, LLP one of the largest law firms in the Country and former Undersecretary of the Treasury of the United States. He also was a star quarterback of his college team and inducted into their Hall of Fame. Let's welcome Bill Chambers."

After a round of applause.

Bill Chambers: "Thank you for having me, I appreciate the opportunity to be here. First a little of my back ground not mentioned by your professor. When I was not much older than you are today, I went to law school and following graduation moved to Los Angles with no money and no job. Not yet a member of the California bar I went straight from the airport to the largest law firm in the City figuring I might as well start at the top. I knew the firm only interviewed law students in the top tier of their graduating class and from the top law schools and never talked to walk-ins, but I convinced the secretary to get me five minutes with the hiring manager of the firm. When he asked me why I should be considered, I told him I would work as a free intern until I passed the California Bar and if I didn't pass on the first try I would shake his hand and move on with no drama. The California Bar is known to be one of the toughest Bar exams in the Country and he liked my confidence so he agreed to hire me not as an unpaid intern, but as a paid legal assistant. He then told me I could start the next day. But I had to tell him I didn't even have a place to stay or any money and luckily he advanced me enough to get an apartment and some new clothes.

After passing the Bar on my first go, I quickly rose through the ranks from associate to head of their M&A department and when I doubled the department's revenues over the next couple of years they offered me a partnership paying eight hundred and fifty thousand dollars a year and that was back when eight hundred and fifty thousand dollars was a lot of money and it usually took many more years to make partner. But I turned them down, because by then I knew I wanted to be my own boss. I walked away from the security of a lot of money and opened my own investment banking firm.

Growing up I had an abusive dominating father who never gave me any compliments no matter how well I did in school or sports. Because of this I poured my efforts into everything I did hoping that my success would force him to say 'good job son.' I wanted his approval more than anything. On the day I got inducted into my college's football Hall of Fame I caught him smiling and that was the only recognition I ever got.

After that I had only one goal in life and that was to make a lot of money. I didn't care about a work/life balance or anything else, I only wanted to get rich no matter what it took figuring he would have to recognize me then. Money was the only thing on my mind.

My uncle who invented a plastic fastener used in construction had become very wealthy. He knew of my goal and told me 'Bill if you really want to become rich don't get married until you've made your fortune, because a wife and children will not only consume a lot of your time and money, but limit your opportunities. What if you had this great opportunity and it required you to relocate and your wife didn't want to go?'

So I took his advice got very rich, sold my company and retired at the age of thirty five. I was living at the beach in Malibu, CA with a vacation home in the south of France and a 152 foot yacht. After traveling the world and living a partying lifestyle, I decided it was time to settle down and started looking for a wife. I remembered a beautiful girl I had seen on my trips to Italy who worked in a restaurant I frequented, so I flew back and long story short convinced her to marry me. We now have four daughters which motivated me to go back to work. So I started another investment bank and subsequently other related businesses. My advice to you MBA students just starting out and wanting to make a lot of money is to stay focused and don't limit your choices before you even get started. I'll pause here to answer any questions?"

Student: "Mr. Chambers, since you said you were focused solely on making money, would you say that you are happy? And, looking back, would you do anything differently."

Bill Chambers: "You can call me Bill. My answer is yes and no. I'm married to a beautiful woman and have four amazing, expensive, entitled daughters and over one hundred million dollars' worth of personal homes alone so I succeeded in reaching my goal. But I have a level of responsibility I've never encountered before and have to consider my family before I can do anything which is why I advised you like my uncle advised me, not to do anything that might limit your choices. As far as looking back, sometimes I'm very happy and other times I'm not so sure. But I will say this, no matter how much money you have, life is full of ups and downs, nonetheless there's an old saying 'I've been rich and I've been poor, rich is better.'"

Student: "Bill, what advice do you have for someone like me to achieve financial independence at an early age like you did, besides not to get married?"

Bill Chambers: "It is difficult to become wealthy working for a salary, because it's limited and after taxes you are not left with very much. That's not to say that CEOs of big corporations aren't making a lot of money and with very little risk to themselves, but you need to start your own company or take over another because when you increase its value it increases your worth exponentially. Let me give you an example. When I started my investment bank I bought a few shares of a small retailer that had half a dozen stores. I was a minority shareholder, but I managed to acquire enough proxies from other shareholders to take over the company, then managed it up and sold it for enough money that I could retire for life if I wanted. So in a little more than two years I made enough money that I would never have to work again. But I took that money and used it to take over a larger retail chain and did the same thing. In less than six years I went from a net worth of a hundred thousand dollars to hundreds of millions of dollars. You don't get that working for some-body else."

Student: "How did you convince the other shareholders to give you their proxies?"

Bill Chambers: "The same way I convinced the hiring man-ager of the law firm to not only give me a job, but pay for my rent, clothing and food. You have to believe in yourself before others can believe in you and you have to know why they are talking to you in the first place."

Student: "Because they believe in you?"

Bill Chambers: "More than that, they want to believe in you. They want to believe you can make them a lot of money and you have to convince them they're right. Of course you have to produce or your career will be over before it really starts."

Student: "I'm interested in doing M&As. What's the best place to start?"

Bill Chambers: "Most people start on the transaction side working for a fee. It's usually pretty hefty, but the fee is limited whereas if you are controlling the company you can make a hell of a lot more."

Student: "But doesn't that takes a lot of capital?"

Mr. Chambers: "The best way to get into the driver's seat is to work for someone else, do a couple of deals with them and not only gain a valuable education, but make some good contacts. Then strike out on your own. When I worked for the Federal government I met with several large pension funds and the people who ran them. Then when I went out on my own I knew the people who held the purse strings to billions of dollars and they knew me."

Student: "If you had to choose one piece of advice for people like us just starting out what would that be?"

Bill Chambers: "Besides what I already said, you need to have a positive money mindset when it comes to creating wealth. Everyone carries a money story and it's your job to understand what yours is and what the other person's is. The right mindset is essential for making money. Money oriented people think differently than people who are not money oriented."

Professor Meyer: "We have time for one more question."

Student: "Bill, are you hiring?"

Bill Chambers: "There's always a job for the right person."

Many students laugh.

Student: "How can we get in touch with you?"

Bill Chambers: "Your professor has my contact information."

Professor Meyer: "Let's show our appreciation to Bill for sharing his sage advice."

Following applause Bill Chambers leaves.

Professor Meyer: "Given our earlier discussion about your desire for a work/life balance I couldn't help noting that your questions to Bill were mostly about how to make money rather than finding that balance."

Student: "Professor, what did you expect we're in B school; it's our conditioning"

The class bursts out in laughter.

Professor Meyer: "Okay, fair enough! As a counter however let's look at a few examples of people who found success simply through their appreciation for their work and life.

The first one is about a man named Arthur Winston who at age 97 spent 70 years cleaning buses. According to an article in the L.A. Times, Mr. Winston who in 1924 at age 17, started cleaning trolley cars for the Los Angeles Railway Co. which ultimately became the Metropolitan Transportation Authority. He quit that job for a spell, then went back on January 24, 1934 and never left. For seventy plus years he worked as a service attendant cleaning the fleet of trolleys then on to buses only missing one day of work the entire time, the day his wife died in 1988. The records show he had never been late, never left early and had never been so sick that 'a gulp of milk of magnesia' couldn't stave off illness or let him drive in the predawn darkness for his shift. At age ninety seven he lived with his twenty six year old great granddaughter and two year old, great, great grandson and woke up each weekday morning at 4:30 to cook his Malt-O-Meal cereal, put on his uniform, then drive his 1978 Oldsmobile Cutlass to the yard. He said he learned the value of work plowing fields with his father in their Oklahoma farm town, "it's good enough" his father told him "just to be a working man." This formed the foundation of his life philosophy, "Working men are simple and humble people. They use the money they earn wisely. They do not rush. They arrive fifteen minutes before every shift. They keep their uniforms crisp. They see to it, even if the boss doesn't ask and the job doesn't call for it that no bus leaves with grimy rims. And they absolutely do not fuss or mope or complain. These values he said, have allowed him to survive. Some of his other words of wisdom were to cut up the credit cards, 'they don't do nothing more than bring about worry, and worry will kill you. And also, 'when folks retire, they end up on the front porch watching the street go by and despair sets in and you're good as gone.'"

Student: "Professor, that's an amazing story, but don't you think there's a different culture between blue collar and white collar responsibly to society?"

Professor Meyer: "I think they are interrelated. You might recall that very relationship is discussed in Schumacher's book *Small Is Beautiful* where Schumacher explains why one cannot exist without the other and one is not more important than the other. But more to the point of bringing this story to your attention is that success is finding fulfillment and has little to do with money and more to do with what the Buddhists call *right work* meaning to engage in a compassionate activity and make your living in a way that does not cause harm and is ethically positive. Consider the words Arthur Winston used, 'it's good enough just to be a working man' which I take to mean he is appreciative that he has a job that is of service to others and provides him with the basic comforts in life. We all die and none of us can take any materialism with us, 'there are no U-Haul's behind a hearse.' No matter how much you may accumulate during your lifetime, at the time of your death you and Arthur Winston will have the same amount.' And too, his work ethic, 'arrive early, be diligent, see to it, even if the boss doesn't ask and the job doesn't call for it, that you take pride in what you do and 'absolutely don't fuss, mope or complain.' Aren't these the same qualities you need to succeed in the white collar world? And his driving an older, but serviceable car and advice on cutting up the credit cards meaning don't spend what you don't have and 'working men are simple and humble people and they use the money they earn wisely', aren't these the same attributes you find in *The Millionaire Next Door?*"

Student: "I see what you mean."

Professor Meyer: "Another story of a successful life is about Herbert S. Kirk a WWI pilot who died at 106 years of age. He graduated from Montana State University with a degree in art at age 97, becoming the oldest graduate in the school's history. At age 104, he was one of several American veterans of WW1 awarded the Legion of Honor, Frances highest award for his part in preserving France during WW1. A strong athlete throughout his life he was an active runner well past the age of 100. At the age of 90 he went for hour-long runs four to five mornings a week covering about four miles each time. At the age of 104 he also became the oldest man to complete the annual Montana Governor's 5K race. And he was an avid tennis play until his early nineties when his eyesight started to decline and he had trouble seeing the ball; that's when he took up running. While the article did not discuss his business life or source of income its importance to this lesson is, that he continued to live life to the fullest; to push himself and learn versus putting his efforts into making more money or sitting back and indulging himself.

Student: "That's unbelievable. Not many people live that long yet alone do the things that he has done."

Professor Meyer: "Of course not all of us will be fortunate enough to enjoy the level of physical and mental health he had, but I retell this story to underscore the wisdom of Arthur Winston's advice about retirement, that is, 'When folks retire, they end up on the front porch watching the street go by, despair sets in and you're good as gone' meaning when you lose purpose in life you cease to find fulfillment.' Mr. Kirk continued to find purpose. He embraced life like a young man until the day he died. So when you consider your goal to make a lot of money and retire young, you should also include a plan that is going to enrich your life and that of others going forward or else you just might end up 'as good as gone'"

Student: "Professor in another class, four of the five guest speakers said there is no such thing as a work/life balance.

One of the speakers, a woman mentioned that she retired recently, because she did not want to repeat with her grandsons, the mistakes she made with her son, meaning she had put work before her family. Another executive said that he retired at age fifty two because he realized he didn't know his kids.

It's mind boggling for me to hear that people who obviously have missed a huge part of their kids' lives are saying that we should not expect to have a work/life balance and should not even approach the topic with the company during the first five or ten years of our career."

Professor Meyer: "Hearing that reminds me of a newly minted lawyer I met a few years ago who went to work for a large law firm in New York City because they started new associates like him off with a very high salary. In exchange for this he worked eighteen hours a day seven days a week often sleeping at the office. He told me that among the perks the firm provided to new associates like him, were meals picked up at local restaurants and delivered to him at the office, his laundry and dry cleaning picked up at the office and returned there, and on days he didn't sleep at the office, a car and driver picked him up and drove him home then a few hours later picked him up and drove him back to the office. When he joined the firm he was told by other associates not to expect a weekend off for the first five years. Besides the high starting salary, the carrot on the stick was that someday he might climb the ladder from junior associate to associate partner to full partner which at the time meant a minimum compensation of nine hundred thousand year.

When I asked him if the full partners seemed happy, he shared his observation that they seemed dead inside and often ate lunch alone. That young lawyer made a choice to sacrifice his work/life balance for a bigger pay check and sometimes that may be a good short term decision, but the danger is that all too often the short term becomes longer and longer as the pay check becomes more important and the work/life balance goal is forgotten or pushed further down the road. It's a slippery slope. How do you think you can avoid this happening to you?"

Student: "By taking the advice from *The Millionaire Next Door,* be frugal and don't spend what I don't have on things I don't need. That way needing and wanting more money won't dominate my choices."

Professor Meyer: "Yes, that's definitely one way to keep your values in the forefront. Now I would like you consider the choses others have made in their quest to lead a successful, fulfilling life. Mary Ann Russell was born into a wealthy San Francisco family. Her father Donald chaired the Southern Pacific Railroad. Her sister passed away at a young age leaving Mary Ann the only heir to the family fortune. In 1948 she married Richard K. Miller who was an heir to the Folger coffee fortune. His grandfather was the founder of Pacific Lighting Corporation which became Pacific Gas and Electric Company which today is better known as PG&E and Richard became a vice president of that company. Together they had ten children and were prominent socialites in San Francisco with Mary Ann holding board positions on some twenty two organizations. She presided over frequent parties at their nine-bedroom San Francisco mansion overlooking the Bay and spent her days drinking champagne, smoking, playing cards and traveling around the world on scuba diving trips. Her friends included an 'A' list of celebrities like Ronald and Nancy Reagan and many others. On her 61st birthday, after Richard had passed away, she announced she would be entering a convent and threw one last party at her mansion just before selling it to a member of the band *Metallica*. Eight hundred people attended the party to see Mary Ann wearing a crown of flowers and carrying a helium balloon so that people could find her in the crowd. She then gave away all of her possessions and boarded a plane the next day to join *The Sisters of Our Lady of Mount Carmel* based in Des Plaines, Illinois announcing to her friends and family that 'The first two-thirds of my life were devoted to the world. The last third will be devoted to my soul.' She remained in the convent for the rest of her life, rarely seeing her family."

Student: "Wow, I can't image anyone doing that, giving up all that wealth and lifestyle."

Professor Meyer: "That's the point of the story; success comes in all forms. It's not just about money and what money can buy for you. It's about experiencing the joy that comes from nourishing the soul.

Here's one more story about a man named Gowtham Kumar Chichil of India who worked in the field of Marketing, but wanted to contribute to society in a meaningful way by helping those poor and less fortunate people who were in need. So at age twenty six he started an NGO called *Serve Needy* to provide free food and services for orphans, personally feeding them and taking care of their dead bodies by performing the last rites, something that was not provided for them. He also ran and continues to run a home for the old-age people, and an orphanage, and recently got himself included into Universal Book of Records for serving food to more than 1000 people in a single day. In addition to this he provides educational services and cares for animals especially cows that are considered sacred in Hindu culture."

Student: "While that level of hands-on devotion and personal sacrifice may not be for me, hearing such a story inspires me to do something with my life other than making money."

Professor Meyer: "That's exactly why I presented these stories."

Student: "And that's why I'm planning to join the Peace Corp after graduation and before starting my career."

Professor Meyer: "I think you will find the Peace Corp very fulfilling aside from any element of government bureaucracy especially if you focus on the aspect of service to others. Here's a Peace Corp related story that might inspire you. I had the good fortune of having lunch with a former president of Peru. There were only four of us at the table and I learned the inspiring story of his background that involved Peace Corp volunteers. He was born into an impoverished indigenous peasant family, the eighth oldest of sixteen brothers and sisters, seven of whom died in childhood. As a child he worked shining shoes and selling newspapers and lottery tickets. At age 11, he finished grade school and his father expected him to leave school and get a job to support the family. His life changed when two Peace Corps volunteers arrived in his village and were drawn to him by his industriousness and charm. They inspired him to apply for a local civic group's scholarship to study in the United States and he was chosen to receive a one-year grant. While in the United States, the two Peace Corp workers helped him get into the University of San Francisco's special program for non-English speakers. Post-graduation he attended Stanford University where he received a MA in Education and a M.A. in Economics of Human Resources and a PhD in human resources. He went on to become the first South American president of indigenous descent to be democratically elected in five hundred years. In addition, he has over fifty honorary doctorates and more awards and accolades than we have time recite having work all over the world teaching at prestigious universities and serving with world leaders at the top level of governments and NGOs. All because of those two Peace Corp volunteers."

Student: "That's an amazing story, I only hope I can help someone in that way."

Professor Meyer: "There are many similar stories and opportunities to do so. Another one that comes to mind, and I won't get into it in great detail due to our time constraints, but you can read about it in a book called *Strength in What Remains* by Tracy Kidder. It's about a young man from Burundi who I also had the good fortune of having dinner with. He barely survived the civil war and genocide in that Country during which many members of his family were killed. After spending months on the run in jungles and refugee camps he arrived in New York City with only $200 in his pocket and not knowing any English or anyone, ended up all alone sleeping in Central Park. He became suicidal describing his experience of sleeping in Central Park and not knowing anyone as 'it made you feel like you were simply not a human being.' Long story short, an elderly man and wife took him into their home, helped him find jobs and ultimately helped him to get into Columbia University and Dartmouth Medical School. He went on to open free medical clinics in his mother country. It's a great read and I highly recommend it. As I said, there are many such stories out there of human kindness toward those in need and I encourage you to become a part of creating new ones.

Moving on. With the limited time we have left today I feel a need to emphasize the following. The two disciplines of Mantra and Meditation will go a long way toward assuring you will have a successful work/life balance, but it is important to remember they will not prevent you from experiencing stress, only how to deal with it in a healthy way. No matter how you live your life it will be full of challenges, that's how we grow, that's how we fulfill our purpose of returning to the experiential awareness of unity which is our common core; if there were no challenges we would not be motivated to search for a better way of living, one that will ultimately reunite us with this common core. This is the lesson in the Bible where god reminds us of our place in the greater scheme of things when he tells Adam and Eve after they ate the forbidden fruit from the tree of the knowledge (which again represents the duality of the phenomenal world versus the unity of the spiritual world), 'By the sweat of your face you shall eat bread, till you return to the ground, for out of it you were taken; for you are dust and to dust you shall return.'

You will still have to get up in the morning and go to work and take care of responsibilities even when you don't feel like it. You will still get sick, although likely less if you meditate regularly. Your loved ones will still get sick. You will still have to deal with money issues and the death of loved ones. There will be days when things won't go smoothly at home and days when things won't go smoothly at the office. The car will break down, the refrigerator will go out, the plumbing won't work, people may sue you and you may be accused wrongly. You will win some battles and loose some. The battles will never end, but if your guiding philosophy is to live your life with kindness and forgiveness no matter what comes, you will always find joy because these things are stepping stones leading you back home to unity where all is well and good. This may sound preachy, but consider the alternative of being consumed by self-centeredness and unable to forgive. The philosophy I talk about is a pragmatic one that seems to be the best choice for living a joyful, fulfilling life. As I said at the beginning of this Course if you find another one that works better for you in terms of joy and fulfillment than adopt it.

Your meditation and mantra will always be at your side fighting the good fight for you and giving you the awareness and ability not to be consumed by your challenges. They will keep you centered on what is really important including the capacity to leave the office behind at the end of the work day and give your full attention to your family and friends ready to help them with their problems no matter how tired you may be. This because you will be fueled by the experiential sense of joy that comes from knowing when you help them, you are helping yourself.

In the morning when you wake up and its cold and the last thing you want to do is get out of the warm bed to start another day filled with stressful demands you will have the strength to get up and meditate knowing it is your lifeline and crucial to living a rewarding life. Knowing too, there is no greater gift you can give to your family, friends and the world because it will give you the ability to face any demand with patience, kindness and forgivingness and you will be teaching everyone by example how to experience the joys of life.

Perhaps a good metaphor for the importance of this daily meditation comes from my many years as a flight instructor where a crucial discipline is training a student pilot for the moment they can no longer see the earth's horizon, which is a key reference for spatial orientation. Once a pilot loses sight of the horizon due to obscuring conditions such as clouds or fog, their body and mind will give them confusing and false indications as to spatial orientation and they will not know up from down or right from left. When that occurs the pilot must immediately do something that is very counter intuitive, that is, to shift their focus from outside to inside and fly the aircraft solely by reference to the spatial orientation instruments. Imagine driving your car at a hundred and eighty miles per hour and suddenly you can't see outside the windshield and are told to look only at the instruments on the dashboard. Because this is contrary to our earth bound conditioning it requires retraining our bio computer and instilling a discipline that can only be sustained through regular, consistent practice. You might remember John Kennedy Jr. who crashed into the sea near Martha's Vineyard in 1999 killing himself, his wife and his wife's sister. While Kennedy had received the proper training he did not maintain the discipline and when he lost outside reference due to obscuring weather conditions he failed to respond to it in the appropriate manner. Radar showed his plane climbing and diving, banking right and left indicating he had lost all spatial orientation. Had he maintained the discipline he would not have crashed; there was nothing wrong with the plane. The same was true for the helicopter crash that killed basketball great Kobe Bryant, his teenage daughter and seven others. Only in that case the pilot was skilled in how to deal with spatial disorientation, but he too failed to follow the discipline. As a flight instructor we have a saying, 'the enemy of the new pilot is inexperience. The enemy of the experienced pilot is complacency.' It's similar in martial arts, without continued practice the discipline will not help you when the need arises. And the same goes with using the disciplines of mantra and meditation."

Student: "Professor, what are the signs that will tell us when to switch over to our mantra?"

Professor Meyer: "That's a good question. Let's say you discover someone has got the best of you or disrespected you. Right away your ego is going to tell you, you can't let them get away with it, others won't respect you and you won't respect yourself. Your brain spins on how to get even. Nothing else matters, you lose all perspective and it doesn't matter if the perceived transgression will alter your life or not. It becomes a disease of obsession and you can't think of anything else. Long before you get to that stage, at the first impulse of anger and before you lose sight of your mental horizon, you immediately go for a long walk shifting your attention from the transgression to your mantra which is the spatial orientation instrument that will get you back to flying straight and level. Should the thought of anger or revenge pop up during this process don't give them your attention, instead gently shift back to repeating your mantra. Then, when your mind is calm and clear, if there is something constructive you can do to resolve the issue do it with compassion and kindness knowing you are not only being kind and compassionate to the perceived transgressor, but yourself and additionally fulfilling your spiritual responsibility to be an example for others to follow. Remember Gandhi's sage advice to 'make of your life the world as you want it to be.' And remember the profound example set by Peter Biehl and his wife Linda who forgave the killers of their beloved daughter Amy thereby providing us with a living example of the power of forgiveness to free us from the burden of carrying the transgression and free those too, who have transgressed against us.

This kind of transformation is only possible when you understand life from a spiritual perspective. As Jesus said, when your eye is multiple you see the world around you as separate and cannot help but try to manipulate it to behave the way you want it to be. But when your eye is single you see everyone and everything as one with the indivisible whole. When making choices always ask yourself 'Who will this benefit?' Who will this harm? Is it kind? Is it necessary? Critical thinking should be pursued without fear. What you strive for shows what you value and nothing is of value that does not add to the welfare of the whole; this because you are part of the whole. Are there any more questions or comments before we adjourn?"

Student: "Thank you professor."

Multiple students: "Thank you professor."

Professor Meyer: "Thank all of you. Don't forget to review the books *Lessons from Prison,* and *Ethics in Motion* for next week when we explore Thoughts on Personal Morals and Ethics and hear from our guest speaker who crossed the line and found herself in prison. You won't want to miss her presentation. We stand adjourned."

CLASS FIVE

Thoughts on Personal Morals and Ethics

Professor Meyer: "Welcome back, it's good to see you again. The celebrated poet Maya Angelou said, 'If you're going to live, leave a legacy. Make a mark on the world that can't be erased.' I'm curious, how many of you feel you want to leave a legacy?"

All hands go up.

Professor Meyer: "What would that legacy be?"

Student: "I want to create something that changes the world like Steve Jobs did."

Student: "For me I see my legacy as being a good parent and raising a family that will go on to have their own family."

Student: "I want to help people especially those who are less fortunate."

Professor Meyer: "What I hear in your answers is that each of you see legacy in a different way; innovation that changes society; generations that sustains society; and actions that heal society. For those of you who want to heal society, how do you envision doing that, donating time, money, creating a charity, working for a charitable NGO or foundation?"

Student: "I'm not sure yet, but I think when I make some money I will donate to worthy causes."

Student: "I want to volunteer some of my time. As I said in our previous Class, I'm joining the Peace Corp after I graduate and before starting my career."

Student: "My family already has a foundation and after graduation I will be working at the foundation."

Student: "I want to work for an NGO that helps poor people in underdeveloped countries."

Student: "I'm going to law school after I finish my MBA and want to represent the underrepresented."

Professor Meyer: "I'm encouraged by your responses especially because at the beginning of this Course many of you had expressed a different goal, that of making a lot of money in a short period of time and retiring to a life of self-indulgence. But I sense too, some of you feel you must wait before you can give back. It has been my experience that turning your focus from yourself to the needs of others is more a core philosophy than a future promise. It is also very much a part of the work/life balance necessary for fulfillment in life. Ever since I was a kid I felt a need to give back to others. In grade school I tutored fellow students who had immigrated to the US and were trying to learn English. In college I volunteered at the West Side Children's Center in New York. In the military I taught English as a second language. And when I got married I was a volunteer at an organization for troubled children and a State Park docent even before my wife and I founded the non-profit organization I previously mentioned that transports people in need of medical treatment aboard private aircraft. Besides actively giving, it's also important to share your experiences with others by setting a personal example so they might benefit from the lessons you have learned. Sharing your wisdom through personal example is in many ways more important than your sharing your time and your money, because there is little chance for pretention; it's the wisdom expressed in that saying from Gandhi 'make of yourself the world as you want it to be.' If people, especially children, like what they see in you they will want to emulate it. For example, if you are patient in situations they would not be, they might wonder how this is possible and it just might set them on a path of discovery and transformation. The same can be said for you being forgiving, tolerant, loving, generous and kind in situations where they might react otherwise. Are there any questions or comments so far?"

Hearing none he went on.

Professor Meyer: "In examining our morals and ethics it might once again be helpful to look at the part conditioning plays in what we believe. For example, how many of you feel your life will not be complete unless you have children?"

Most hands go up.

Professor Meyer: "Where do you suppose that feeling comes from? Is it nature or nurture? Why have children? There certainly isn't any shortage of them in the world; the earth's population is exploding. If you feel the need to be maternal or paternal why not adopt? There are plenty of children in need of good homes. Why add to the earth's population when you can save a child in need?"

Student: "Because I want a child of my own."

Professor Meyer: "I'm not judging you, but let's step back for a moment, listen to what you just said and tell me what you hear?"

Student: "Selfishness?"

Professor Meyer: "How many of you reacted to that the same way?"

Several hands go up.

Professor Meyer: "I want to emphasize that we are not here to judge. The only intent in having this conversation is to stimulate critical thinking when it comes to understanding what is behind the choices we make. What do you think is behind wanting children of your own versus adopting a child in need of a good home?"

Student: "It's more the norm, the expected thing to do like growing up, getting married, having children, sending them to college, watching them get married and having your grandchildren?"

Student: "A DNA thing? Our biology to procreate?"

Student: "Our duty to our parents, society and the church?"

Student: "Survival of the species?"

Student: "Leaving a living legacy?"

Student: "If you have a biological child a piece of you doesn't die?"

Professor Meyer: "Perhaps all of those things. The important thing is not whether or not you have children, but that you think critically think about the decision. How many people have children, a life altering decision, without thinking about it just because they believe they're supposed to, then end up resenting the children rather than making the sacrifices necessary to give them uncondi-tional love and properly prepare them for life? Showering them with privilege and money will never be a positive substitute for personal attention and unconditional love. There's wisdom in Hindu literature about raising chil-dren that says 'from birth to the age of five they should be treated like a god. Meaning they should be given all the love, devotion, affection and attention, physically and mentally possible while not surrendering your authority so they can develop the emotional intimacy and security they will need to sustain them later in life.' Some of our mod-ern psychologist suggest that age should be seven. The wisdom further states, 'after age five until the age of six-teen, treat the child as a servant. Meaning to teach them about obedience which will be useful in life since nobody gets their way all the time. Children need and want guid-ance from their parents. They will fight back and rebel as teenagers are known to do, but they need to learn about authority or morals and ethics will escape them.' After age sixteen that Hindu wisdom tells us to treat them as equals. Meaning 'you may argue your opinions, but at the same time listen to them with an open mind and respect. In this way they will feel valued and not afraid to come to you for advice and console.'

The moral and ethical lesson in that guidance is for both parent and child. Without discipline both will not find fulfillment in the world, because life will not bend to each individual's will, they will have to bend to life's will. When I decided to live in the Amazon rainforest cut off from the influences of society to see what I could learn about life, I sought the advice of an Amazonian Indian who told me to survive I would have to adapt to the forest and not try to make the forest adapt to me. As a child he had been taken from his Amazonian home and acculturated into the Christian religion by Jesuits so he was familiar with both cultures including the biblical story of Adam and Eve which he used to illustrate this point and it is why I often use it here in Class. He told me that living in the Amazon is a lot like living in The Garden of Eden, but only if you learn its ways. It was his way of saying 'you can't break the laws of the universe, you can only break yourself against them.' This holds true if we are to live a moral and ethical life knowing there are consequences for every action. Are there any questions so far?"

Hearing none he continued.

Professor Meyer: "There's a parable I found on the Internet about the importance of achieving a work/life balance that's foundational to a moral and ethical life. It is about a professor who stood before his philosophy class with a very large, but empty jar and proceeded to fill the jar with golf balls. He then asked the students if the jar was full. They agreed it was.

The professor then picked up a box of pebbles and poured them into the jar. He shook the jar until the pebbles filled in the open areas between the golf balls. He then asked the students again if the jar was full and they agreed it was.

The professor then picked up a box of sand and poured it into the jar and the sand filled up everything else. He then asked the students if the jar was full and they agreed it was.

The professor then produced two cups of coffee and poured them into the jar filling the empty space between the sand.

He then said, 'I want you to recognize that the Jar represents your life. The golf balls are the important things in your life – your family, your children, your health, your friends and your favorite passions – and if everything else was lost and only they remained, your life would still be full.

The pebbles are the other things that matter like your job, your house, and your car.

The sand is everything else, the small stuff, if you put the sand into the jar first there would be no room for the pebbles or the golf balls. The same goes for life. If you spend all your time and energy on the small stuff you will never have room for the things that are important to you.

Pay attention to the things that are critical for your happiness. Play with your children. Take time to get medical checkups. Take your spouse out to dinner. Play another round of golf. There will always be time to clean the house and fix the disposal. Take care of the golf balls first, the things that really matter. Set your priorities, the rest is sand.'

One of the students then asked what about the coffee. The professor replied, 'I'm glad you asked. It just goes to show you that no matter how full your life may seem, there's always room for a couple of cups of coffee with a friend.'

Personally I have always been intrigued by the fascination with fame and consumption that our society seems to have – in large part due to the persuasive bearing of commercial marketing – which has an influence on our morals and ethics. For example, and I use this often because it is so prevalent, how people struggling to make ends meet go out and spend money in detriment to their own needs and those of society, to have a particular item such as a pair of sneakers or a shirt just because a famous person's name is attached to them. Or spend a lot of money to go to a concert to be in the same space as someone they have never met; particularly when they could hear and see the same thing for free on TV or the Internet. And if that sports hero or performer has a tattoo they run out and get a similar tattoo. And if he or she wears their hair long, they wear their hair the same way. Instead of discovering their own identity, they emulate others. I recently met a salesman in a sneaker store, a young man likely working for minimum wage or close to it, who was wearing an unusual pair of sneakers. Upon inquiry he told me he paid $450 for them at a store that only sells used sneakers and that their original cost when new was $180, but they had become so trendy they were valued at far more than he had paid. What people choose to do with their money is not of my concern, but if creating financial independence is your goal these are a few examples of what not to do."

Student "Professor, I read an article on actor Nicolas Cage's financial problems and how he caused his own ruin by an addiction to spending. According to the article he bought fifteen expensive palatial homes plus two castles, several yachts, nine Rolls Royce's, a Gulfstream Jet, more than a dozen purchases of expensive jewelry and forty seven purchases of artwork and exotic items in addition to taking his sizable entourage on costly vacations and throwing huge expensive parties at his homes. His business manager claims to have warned him that he needed to earn thirty million dollars a year 'just to maintain his lavish lifestyle and that he was living beyond his means.'"

Student: "I read one about the effects of exposure to luxury goods on cognition and decision making. The authors found that exposure to luxury goods increases a person's propensity to prioritize self-interest above the interests of other's and influences the decisions they make in their personal and business lives that benefit themselves to the detriment and potential harm of others. The authors conducted experiments to find out if those who are surrounded by luxury in their personal and corporate lives would tend to be less concerned about others than themselves, and what they discovered was that they tend to place self-interest above societal interest. If they could make a decision that might harm society yet yield more comfort and luxury to themselves they would do so. They were not out to harm others nor did they want to, but if it came to more for me against a potential harm to others they would go for the self-interest."

Professor Meyer: "That is why we are having this discussion in a class about moral and ethics."

Student: "Professor, in my marketing class we discussed an article about how we are manipulated into spending, the author lists all the tricks sellers use to get shoppers to part with their money. The tricks were all well founded in extensive research. Many of them centered on our five senses, seeing, hearing, touching, tasting, and smelling. For seeing, merchandise was displayed in a manner that looks better in the store than it does when you get it home. For hearing, the music and the tempo of the music was selected to appeal to the demographic buyer who would most likely purchase the merchandise based on the music being played as their type of music; the tempo of the music was deliberately selected to keep people in the store, the slower the tempo the longer they might linger. As to taste and smell, you can imagine how scents could trigger salivary glands and trigger hunger thoughts. For touch, it gives you pleasure to touch something and think it could be yours. The article also talked about the power of point of purchase on impulse buying, that while you are waiting to check out, items call out for you to take them as you approach the register, even if you don't need them or particularly want them. They are priced right and offered in an enticing way. The article also covered following the herd buyers and pricing to appear that it is a bargain you can't pass up. Lastly, it covered how using credit and debit cards have a way of getting people to spend more than if they were parting with cash."

Professor Meyer: "All the tricks of the trade to separate you from your hard earned money and make money central to your moral and ethical decisions."

Student: "I read an article on how moving from lower income to lower middle income increases happiness. After that, increases in disposable income didn't seem to increase happiness, but spending a little of this money on others did."

Professor Meyer: "That conforms to studies that indicate the less self-centered we are, the happier we are."

Student: "My girlfriend and I had a discussion on *The Money Trap* where the authors talk about 'Making a living or making a dying; compromising our dreams to make a living.' We felt when our focus was only on making a living, not only did it affect our work/life balance, but our morals and ethics as well, since it is easier to lose sight of the forest for the trees. *The Money Trap* centers on buying into advertising messages; what marketers think about the ethicality of the marketing campaigns they create; how the money trap can be devastating to a person, causing depression and creating a world where we have extreme separation between our work and our lives."

Student: "The book also talks about how we become our jobs and that more work produces less savings and more debt. And why hasn't more work resulted in more savings and less debt? And how the quality of life is correlated to income. It's because of the 'more is better' philosophy that drives us as consumers."

Professor Meyer: "That's what President Hebert Hoover's analysis of consumerism reportedly said, 'wants are insatiable and the consumer was created to consume the products created by the industrial revolution.' And industrialist Henry Ford's philosophy 'When people work less they buy more.' Based on this he shocked the country by doubling the average daily pay of his workers to $5.00 so they could afford to buy the cars they were making. While a certain level of growth can be good, we need to change from the ethic of growth to the ethic of sustainability which shifts self-interest to pan-interest. This requires that we transform our relationship with money. The fulfillment curve of 'enough' is a good place to start and end. Consumer consciousness is central to the phenomenal world while morals and ethics are central to the spiritual world."

Student: "That's what the author meant in his comments on 'enough' and 'things' versus 'activities' where he said once you realize 'enough' and 'things' you can begin to get rid of things that over burden and stifle your life rather than enhance it.'"

Student: "In chapter one, the author begins with an illustration of the so called 'old road map for money', a view on how many people tend to live their lives centered on money and achievement. Given this view, the author proposes that we might subconsciously value money more than our life or life itself. Based on this he suggests that by living a money-centered lifestyle we are actually making a dying rather than a living."

Student: "And he suggests that money is the life of many people as they are spending the great majority of their days working in jobs; some that they might not even like. Do we come home from work energized and refreshed? No! For a lot of us the dreams we initially had about working in a fulfilling job have gradually become the reality of professional politics, burnout, boredom and intense competition. Furthermore, personalities are converging with job positions and proclaimed achievements have become increasingly materialistic creating a significant amount of peer pressure and the consequences are work related depression, anxiety and stress."

Professor Meyer: "You may wonder what discussing these things has to do with today's lesson on personal morals and ethics, but self-centeredness is antagonist to morals and ethics. I don't play golf, but a good friend of mine had a nice home on a very nice golf course and I once took two friends who were ardent golfers there to meet and play golf with him. The friend who hosted us, was retired and enjoyed golf as a pleasant pass time, but my two other friends were high achieving businessmen executives who played golf like they conducted business that is to say, very intense and competitive. Every time they hit the ball, good shot or not, they got angry at themselves and defensive for not doing better. My retired friend finally gave them a piece of advice that went something like this, 'nobody cares how you play because they are only thinking about how they play'. At the end of the day one of my intense golfer friends who was the president of a major motion picture studio division said to me, 'you have such a nice friend and he seems to enjoy life. For me, every day when I go to the office, I know there will come a time when I will be standing on my desk screaming my lungs out, yelling at somebody for something.' That friend made a couple of million dollars a year, always flew aboard a private jet, had a huge house in an upscale neighborhood and another at the beach in Malibu. I almost said he 'lived' in a huge home', but he didn't spend much time in it, nor was it a sanctuary because he always carried the office with him wherever he went. He also had a wife and a daughter who he hardly saw or knew. He ultimately died in his mid-sixties leaving his wife and daughter in debt not because he didn't earn a lot of money, but he had an expensive lifestyle and even though he had investments and insurance when the primary income stopped the enormous bills kept coming. To him morals and ethics where weaknesses in others that he could exploit for his own gain."

Student: "In *Your Money or Your Life* the authors said that the positive effects of a high consumer lifestyle are few. That making a high income living does not translate into significant wealth. The savings rate in the United States has declined from ten percent in the 1980s to almost zero percent today. That the culture of spending and consumption requires us to go along with the established nine to five routines and keep unwanted jobs. We assume that we work to pay the bills, but we spend more on stuff that we do not need, so we have to work to earn more money. This does not lead to happiness, but rather to constant desire for more, independent of the respective income levels. "

Professor Meyer: "The pressure of debt and obsessive consumption weaken our resistance to crossing the line into immoral and unethical behavior as we will hear later on today from our guess speaker."

Student: "Professor, that's exactly why the authors say a new road map for money is needed. We have to learn to free ourselves from the irrational monetary thought patterns that govern our lives and tell us that more money equals more fulfillment. They offer that one part of the solution is to find a level of fulfillment that is sufficient and can be categorized as having 'enough' money. And that we free ourselves from the various forms of clutter that we do not need in order to feel fulfilled."

Professor Meyer: "Some psychologist categorize hoarding as a mental health problem; the need to get more, even if you already have a lot."

Student: "That's the point the authors make. They propose we make peace with the past by calculating how much we have earned in our lives and determine what we have to show for it. This includes making a checklist of all the income we ever had, then creating a personal balance sheet listing our current assets and liabilities from big items such as real estate and cars to the money in our wallets. The subtraction of liabilities from the accumulated assets will then represent our monetary net worth. An important principle while going through the process is not to judge or blame ourselves for the monetary mistakes of the past."

Student: "Professor I can take it from there. In the second chapter of the book the authors deal with the concept of money. From their point of view, money goes beyond its physical form of a nation's currency. To widen our horizons in terms of what money is, they introduce four relevant perspectives using the metaphor of a city skyscraper.

The street level perspective of what money is encompasses a practical and physical definition. This refers to the way in which we use money every day and includes the whole range of financial transactions we encounter during our lives. This is also the level where most financial problems are located and where we frequently look for solutions to solve these problems; often just to create more or different problems.

Next is *the neighborhood perspective* based on the psychological or emotional realm where we are at a high enough level to detect behavioral patterns instead of detailed actions. This encompasses how we think and feel about money; our individual attitude toward it in general. For example, do we perceive it as a form of security or power or social acceptance or as evil?

Next is the *citywide perspective* it deals with the cultural realm of money. It acknowledges the fact that the perception of money can be a cultural thing. This means that not only individual assumptions exists, but that there are collective assumptions that we all share. For example this could be the view of money as a means of exchange or an instrument to store value. The economic concepts of cost of living, inflation, recession or depression belong to this realm as well. Although many cultures have similar assumptions about money, the importance of the concepts varies. One assumption frequently observed in the United States is that more is better and growth is good. This perspective is partially responsible for the unhappiness described in the first chapter and can be critically questioned for this level of observation."

Student: "I'll take the last perspective which is *the helicopter perspective* of money or the realm of personal responsibility and transformation. The purpose of this point of view is to return to us the power we have unconsciously given over to money. This means we realize it is possible to leave our cultural boundaries, the citywide point of view, and the view of money as an external influence behind. We should adopt the perspective that money is something we deliberately choose to trade our life energy for and should therefore create enough value to be worth it. We ultimately pay for money with our finite lifetime which should make us think whether we, for example, really want to keep jobs we do not like just for the money's sake. Money should be included in our lives with purpose and we should attempt to free our emotional states from our economic fortune. The second step proposed by the authors is to be in the present and track your life energy. This can be achieved by following two steps. First, it is important to determine one's real hourly wage. This does not refer to the wage you earn per hour at work, but to the net wage that is left over after subtracting all expenses required to maintain this job. The result does not only pose the question whether one hour of life energy is worth this wage, but also shows how much life energy has to be traded in for one dollar of expenditure. In a calculation example a person earning six hundred and fifty dollars a week was left with less than six dollars per hour of work after adjusting this wage for job-related expenses."

Professor Meyer: "That's an excellent point. How many people do you see commuting in expensive cars that they have to work years just to pay for while it's depreciating in value? My commute each day and I am fortunate, is only seven miles each way. If I purchase a sixty thousand dollar car with the cost of maintenance, fuel, taxes and annual registration etc. it would cost in terms of after tax earnings and lost opportunity on the cash, a good deal of my finite lifetime just to drive that fourteen miles a day round trip notwithstanding some non-work related driving. So I have to ask myself does working for the car instead of the car working for me make any sense. Another view is, I could retire years earlier simply by driving a less expensive car. You might remember that our guest speaker Mr. Amadi a high net worth individual, purchased a used car because he recognized that it is a depreciating asset."

Student: "The author's second sub-step of the money perspective is the same as the journal exercise we did for this Class, it requires us to keep track of every cent that comes and goes into our life. The creation of the personal *Daily Money Log* has the purpose of helping us to become conscious of how we spend the money that we trade our life for. This way we can become aware of the expenditures that are worth the investment and those that are not."

Professor Meyer: "Some of you might recall a movie entitled *In Time* where in place of money, each person was given a certain amount of time to live and that time, like a clock, was displayed on their arm. It was their personal bank account of life, like gas in the tank of a car, and when it was gone their life was over. This is similar to what the Hindus call *Prana*, the amount of life energy we receive at birth. And it's a good way of looking at our lives in terms of how much *Prana* do we want to spend toward making money?"

Student: "In *The Compassionate Universe* Easwaran, makes the following points to use as a guide to individual morality and ethics. That no life is insignificant so treat every part of nature with love and respect. Human beings need to be interconnected to the entirety of the world. That a compassionate universe is not about competition, but cooperation with artistry and thrift. And that success does not shield us against the ups and downs of life. He then offers as guidance Mahatma Gandhi's seven social sins:

1. *Knowledge without character:* The lack of connection between what we know is good for us and our ability act on that knowledge.
2. *Science without humanity:* Where production, consumption and national boundaries are more important than people or the earth.
3. *Wealth without work:* Regarding young people with no idea or goal worthy of their ambition.
4. *Commerce without morality:* The addiction to profit, but no human need or environmental need.

5. *Politics without principles:* The lack of faith in human nature.
6. *Pleasure without conscience:* A destructive life style based on that lack of faith.
7. *Worship without self-sacrifice:* Wherein we overlook the most precious evolutionary resources; idealism, sensitivity to the suffering of others and the sense of unity."

Professor Meyer: "I recommend that each of you download and keep a copy of these; it's a wonderful check list for moral and ethical behavior both in your personal life and in the work you choose to do."

Student: "Eswaran goes on to say that we tend to try to solve more complicated problems than simple life challenges such as how to live together in peace and good health. And that we don't understand what our needs are and treat every problem as if it were a matter of technology, chemistry or economics. Stressing too, that in our society there is an exaggerated importance of profit in a business, citing how agriculture became agribusiness and everything has to do with how to make the most profit."

Professor Meyer: "Think about this in terms of sustainability. In businesses that are owned and run by families and/or sole proprietors, the primary objective is to make a living. But in businesses that are run by corporations the primary objective is not just making a profit, but perpetually increasing profits."

Student: "Yes, increasing those profits for each quarter and every quarter ad infinitum."

Professor Meyer: "Exactly as if such a trajectory is sustainable! Two stories come to mind to further illustrate this. The first is about the former Las Vegas and the current Las Vegas. In the former Las Vegas the hotel rooms, the food, the drinks, the lounge shows, use of the pool and other amenities were all very inexpensive to the consumer because the casinos were privately owned and the owners were satisfied with making very nice profits from the gambling. Then came corporate ownership and with it the need to make every amenity a profit center. Now Las Vegas is very expensive to visit; virtually nothing is free or offered at a low cost.

The second story is about a man who designed a new type of cardboard box that would make it easier to take home food from fast food restaurants and store any leftovers. It was a brilliant idea and you would think every fast food restaurant chain in the world would want to use it, but it cost three cents more than the boxes they were currently using so they would not buy it, because their business model was not about food or customers, but profits and three cents multiplied by the millions of boxes per year compromised that profit. The corporations do not even refer to what their restaurants serve as food, but product. What else does Easwaran say about profits?"

Student: "Profits above all else has led to the use of chemicals for crops to increase yield even though these chemicals are dangerously effecting the environment and the crops themselves. And the 'more is better' mentality has led us to wanting more in every facet of our lives. After our basic needs are met we still want more. We want to be 'somebody' and to feel secure and this systematically leads to wanting more possessions. We have become servants to our own unintended greed. Consumption has become our master and a way of life. To break this cycle we need to make the connection between what we know is healthy and what we do in our daily lives."

Professor Meyer: "Thank you for that. Now is a good time for us to hear the report on an article written by renowned innovation expert Clayton Christensen on *"How will you measure your life?"*

Student: "The article Professor Meyer assigned me to report on is from Harvard Business School professor Clayton Christensen who teaches his students not just how to succeed in business, but in life much like Professor Meyer does in this Course.

In the article Professor Christensen talks about how to live a life of integrity and stay out of jail and how the marginal cost of doing something 'just this once' always seems to be negligible, but the full cost is typically much higher. When that occurs a voice in our head says, 'look, I know that as a general rule, most people shouldn't do this. But in this particular extenuating circumstance, just this once, it's okay.' It suckers you in and you don't see where it is leading you, and in the end you pay for it dearly.

He gives an example of the twenty six year old trader who brought down the two hundred and thirty three year old British merchant bank *Barings* after racking up one point three billion dollars in trading losses before being detected. It began with one small decision that turned out to be a relatively small error, but the young trader didn't want to admit his mistake and tried to cover it up which led him down a deeper and deeper path of deception of lies, forged documents, misleading auditors and making false statements to try and cover up the mounting losses. Eventually, he and *Barings* arrived at their day of reckoning. He was arrested, the Bank was forced into bankruptcy and sold for just one pound. Twelve hundred employees lost their jobs, some of them friends of the trader, and he was sentenced to six and a half years in prison. As soon as he took that first step there was no longer a boundary where it made sense to him, to turn around. The first step is always a small one until it reaches a point of no return.

Professor Christensen goes on to say that in terms of not crossing the line, 'one hundred percent of the time, is easier than ninety eight percent of the time.' Meaning that many of us might convince ourselves that we are able to break our own personal ethics 'just this once' by justifying a small choice or choices. That first choice does not seem to be a major issue, but once that line has been crossed it disappears and we are lost in a space without boundaries. His advice is to 'decide what you stand for and stand for it one hundred percent of the time.'

His peers who reviewed the article had some good advice too. Here are some of their comments:

1. 'The slippery slope of that 'just this once' is seen frequently in many frauds.'
2. 'I had many arguments with people who cherry pick and vacillate when it comes to principals.'
3. 'Our lives cannot be compartmentalized into business vs. personal, money vs. ethics, spiritual vs. practical. Indeed such compartmentalization is another way to miss the full cost of our decisions.'
4. 'Our life is measured by our strength to stand firm on our basic principles, truth, honesty, morality, ethics and adherence to whatever is right. We must never compromise on these principals despite the short-term lure of some advantages which in the foreseeable future will lead us to doom.'
5. 'There do come occasions when we feel that we will not be caught if we very cleverly and intelligently commit a somewhat wrong action for big gain, just this once. Yes we may never be caught. There commences a vicious circle of repetition for we start believing that our actions are catch proof. Such actions finally snowball to an unmanageable level and there is a great fall.'
6. 'Making compromises to what you know is right is a death of a 1000 cuts.'
7. 'Right means lead to right results, wrong means never lead to right results.'
8. 'We get so caught up in making money we forget our goal, a world that works.'
9. 'I like the message, but it implies that once you cross the line there is no hope for you. I developed a theory

of ethics back in my teens when I often observed adults stating one thing and doing another. As I have grown and experienced life I find it rare for anyone to practice one hundred percent ethical behavior. I do believe you can strive to meet your principles. If on rare occasion you do falter and cross the line in the sand (your personal ethical boundary) as long as you recognize you crossed the line and strive not to do so again, the line in the sand remains. However if you justify your crossing the line in the sand, the line in the sand of what is considered unethical, shifts to a new location of what that person now perceives as unethical. Each subsequent crossing and justification will see that line continue to shift further and further into what that person would have once considered truly unethical behavior.'

10. 'I remember a character in a classic Hindi novel saying 'I have chalked my own paths in life and at times when I reached the wrong destination, traced my steps back and started all anew.''"

Professor Meyer: "Thank you for that great report. It is not saying stick to your decisions no matter what, you should always learn and adapt to changing circumstances, but the foundation for all those decisions should be your own moral and ethical values. It might be easier for you not to think in terms of right or wrong which can be rationalized, but rather to remember there are inescapable consequences built in to every decision you make; it's another way of saying god or the spiritual universe is omnipresent.

To be fair I should mention there are other schools of thought on ethics. Philosophers have studied and argued about ethics for hundreds if not thousands of years and those arguments can get very heady. My objective in the Course is to be pragmatic and not over intellectualize the subject, but I will offer up two of the main schools of ethical philosophy to make you aware of them and perhaps provoke further thought on the subject. One of them is called *Deontology*. Deontology is an ethical theory that says actions are good or bad according to a clear set of rules. And that the morality of an action should be based on whether that action itself is right or wrong under the series of rules and principles, rather than based on the consequences of the action. It is sometimes described as duty, obligation, or rule-based ethics. To some this may mean that your duty or obligation under a set of rules trumps any consequences. Think of a soldier's actions during war; think also of the arguments made at the Nuremberg trials. Deontologists argue that you can never know what the results will be so it doesn't make sense to decide whether something is ethical based on outcomes. Essentially, do the right thing; do it because it's the right thing to do; don't do wrong things; avoid them because they are wrong.

The other main school is *Utilitarian Ethics* where outcomes justify the means or ways to achieve it. Utilitarianism determines right from wrong by focusing on outcomes. It is a form of consequentialism. Utilitarianism holds that the most ethical choice is the one that will produce the greatest good for the greatest number.

So how do you decide? Let's look at the primary goal of ethics which is to help resolve questions of human morality by defining concepts such as good and evil, right and wrong, virtue and vice, justice and crime. One such effort is presented in an article entitled, *12 Ethical Principles for Business Executives* by Michael Josephson as follows:

1. HONESTY. Be honest in all communications and actions.
2. INTEGRITY. Maintaining personal integrity.
3. PROMISE-KEEPING. Keep promises and fulfill commitments.
4. LOYALTY. Be loyal within the framework of other ethical principles.
5. FAIRNESS. Strive to be fair and just in all dealings.
6. CARING. Demonstrate compassion, a genuine concern for the well-being of others.
7. RESPECT FOR OTHERS. Treat everyone with respect. Law abiding, obey the law.
8. COMMITMENT TO EXCELLENCE. Pursue excellence all the time in all things
9. LEADERSHIP. Exemplify honor and ethics
10. REPUTATION AND MORALE. Maintain a good reputation for high moral values.
11. ACCOUNTABILITY. Be accountable."

Student: "I once read that every individual has two possessions of his own. His physical body and his soul. The physical body needs the pleasure of material possessions and as these possessions increase it wants more of them so we are never satisfied. The soul is always striving for joy and peace that can only be gained through moral and ethical means."

Professor Meyer: "That's a good segue into our next subject, one that was on many of your pre-class assignment on moral and ethical issues that concern you today and that is the issue of sex, more specifically the role it plays in the process of personal decisions.

I presume some of you have experienced the intensity of sexual desire and if you haven't you've at least heard a good deal about it. Along with money, power and drugs, sex is one of the most compelling forces that influence otherwise moral and ethical people to cross the line into immoral and unethical behavior. We've all heard the stories about the politician, celebrity or corporate officer who gets caught up in a sex scandal. Tony Montana in the movie *Scarface* said 'you gotta make money, which brings power. And once you have power, the women will come.' Many people who acquire those first two things lose their way and seek out sexual encounters in a desperate attempt to fill the void of desire only to discover it doesn't fulfill them. Someone once observed, 'what good is money and power if you can't use them?' However, when power overwhelms judgment people often become involved in things they would be ashamed to admit publically. Remember the prime minister of Italy Silvio Berlusconi who got tried for having sex with a minor. And President Bill Clinton and Monica Lewinsky. And New York governor Eliot Spitzer who had to resign for patronizing an escort service. And in the corporate world CEO of *Uber* Travis Kalanick who was forced to resign from the company he built into one of the giants of Silicon Valley, due to a sex scandal. And Harvey Weinstein who was forced to resign from the board of *The Weinstein Company* one of the most successful film production companies in Hollywood due to allegations of sexual misconduct that ultimately led him to a long prison sentence. And Shervin Pishevar of *Hyperloop One,* co-founder and early *Uber* investor, who lost his job in *Sherpa Capital,* the venture capital firm he co-founded in 2013, following sexual misconduct allegations. And CEO Dave McClure of *500 Startups* who had to quit the tech incubator he helped launch after the New York Times exposed him as a sexual harasser. The newspaper reported that McLure had hit on a job candidate he was trying to recruit. In a mea culpa blog post McClure said he was guilty of taking advantage of many more women adding, 'I made advances towards multiple women in work-related situations, where it was clearly inappropriate' admitting that his behavior was inexcusable and wrong. There are thousands if not hundreds of thousands if not millions of situations where men and women abused their power in a sexual manner. Much if not all of it caused by the absence of a spiritually based moral and ethical compass leaving in its place a delusional belief such as, the abuser must be special otherwise they wouldn't be in the position they are. That consciousness was exemplified by the infamous 'queen of mean' Leona Helmsley – convicted and sentenced to four years in prison, 750 hours of community service and a $7.1 million fine for tax fraud – who famously quipped to one of her lower echelon employees prior to getting caught, 'only the little people pay taxes.'

Absent a foundation anchored in the spiritual realm of unity it is easy for sexual desire to lead us down a pathway of self-destruction rather than enabling us to transform that same energy into a beneficial force. It's not that sex or sexual desire is in itself destructive, but how that energy is utilized. Using an analogy of electrical energy, it can make our morning toast or be used to put someone to death. It's the same energy utilized differently.

According to the Internet, the typical White-collar criminal is a mid-40s male, married and likely didn't commit their first criminal act until their late 30s. The business losses that are caused by executives of companies are sixteen times higher than the business losses caused by their employees.

Besides sex related misconduct some popular examples of white-collar crimes include securities fraud, embezzlement, corporate fraud, money laundering, identity theft and cybercrimes.

While violent crimes like murder dominate the news and challenge our morals and ethics our attitude toward white-collar crime is a little different. Financial schemes are fascinating and corporate crime is all about context. Cases may come down to whether those accused knew their actions were illegal—which means prosecutors must try to read minds after the fact. For example, the standard defense in a fraud case is not that the fraud didn't happen, it's that the fraudster didn't know he or she was breaking the law, or that, whatever the government may think, the fraudulent behavior is business as usual in that industry.

Drawing these fine lines around intention is even trickier when executives rely on expert advisers to help with their decisions. If a lawyer or an accountant tells you that something is legal—even just barely—should you have to go to jail if he's wrong? Many things that appear greedy or selfish in hindsight are not illegal, and many actual crimes occur when valid business practices edge beyond what the law allows.

Prosecution is especially difficult when criminal behavior spans a whole organization. In such cases it's extremely hard to figure out exactly where the fault lies; think of how often the public fails to distinguish between a corporation and the individuals who work for it. Those high up on the organizational chart, who bear the most responsibility for the company, may know little about its day-to-day activities. And punishing a large company—through massive fines or by sending its most senior leaders to jail—can destroy it, which has serious economic ripple effects for innocent employees, customers, and communities. Most of the crimes involve immoral and unethical activities of the individuals.

Are there any questions so far?"

Hearing none Professor Meyer continues.

Professor Meyer: "Let's take a ten minute break and when you return we'll hear from our guest speaker who did not set out to cross her moral and ethical boundary but did and paid the price."

Following the break.

Professor Meyer: "Our guest speaker Susan Weinstock grew up in the city of Tucson. Her father was a mid-level executive in a construction company and her mother an administrative assistant. Early on she developed an appreciation for the so called finer things in life that some of her high school friends who came from wealthier families had. That led her to choose the potentially high paying profession of Law.

As a twenty nine year old lawyer specializing in business and real estate law, she served as an officer in the local bar association, a partner in a trendy restaurant, drove a top of the line luxury car and lived in a beautiful home not far from her office.

Raised with good moral and ethical values she never considered she would ever cross the line, but she did and found herself in prison as a convicted felon. Here to share her story, please welcome Susan Weinstock."

Following applause.

Susan Weinstock: "Thank you for that warm welcome. As your professor told you, growing up I never thought I would cross the line of good morals and ethics let alone criminal conduct, but I did and spent nearly two years in prison. Like some of you I came from a good middle class family and lived in a good middle class neighborhood. So how did I get there?

Early on I had the ability to talk my way into and out of just about any situation. When I was in high school I approached the bouncer at a concert venue pretending to be the daughter of the music promoter and told him if he did not let me in free of charge he would be in a lot of trouble. To my surprise the charade and many subsequent ones worked so well that when I became a lawyer specializing in business and real estate I was able to talk my way into very profitable transactions that bordered on unethical and illegal boundaries and it became foundational in my approach to everything in life. My willingness to bend the rules and manipulate documents to help myself and my clients resulted in me having a pretty lucrative practice. I often reflected that I made a lot of money by simply writing words on a piece of paper.

As time went on I became increasingly emboldened and when the terrorist attacks of September 11th occurred I found myself applying for a disaster-relief government loan, claiming to have lost the use of an office near Ground Zero which was not true and I received nearly eight hundred thousand dollars.

When the bogus claim was discovered a warrant was issued for my arrest. I was found guilty of perjury, wire fraud and money laundering, and sentenced to twenty four months in prison where I quickly learned some new rules like never take someone's seat in the TV room or ask a fellow prisoner what landed her in prison. I marked my time in custody mostly walking on an outdoor track for three or four hours a day, reading self-improvement books and writing. Time passed slowly. I would often look up at the airplanes flying overhead thinking how the passengers were free to come and go as they wished and I wasn't. When I began my incarceration I never thought of myself as a criminal but as a lawyer and businesswoman whose only crime was not being clever enough to avoid getting caught. This because I knew of many others who did the same or similar things, but did not get caught. I was locked in this personal prison until I finally admitted that what landed me in custody had nothing to do anyone else; it was a crime of my own poor choses. When this happened I was still physically incarcerated, but my soul was free.

By the time I was released I estimated I had walked over seven thousand miles around the track and lost twenty five pounds, but had no idea what to do next.

As a result of the conviction I no longer had a license to practice law or a job. I was a felon and getting hired was not easy. Not only that, the court ordered restitution would take nearly every dollar I might earn. So I volunteered at a free law clinic that helped people like me who had gotten in trouble with the law and needed legal guidance. After a while they hired me and I went full time. It was the best thing that ever happened to me because I was no longer focused on myself, but on the needs of others and felt I was fulfilling an important purpose in life. I now serve as the non-profit's executive director.

Some of the people we help were wrongfully convicted and we work to get their convictions overturned. Others we help by counseling them on how to stay out of trouble while incarcerated and how make the most of their time while inside so that when they get out they have a positive path forward.

One important thing I want to impress upon you from my experience is, that I once had a code of ethics that conformed to the best of society, but my success in getting my way slowly influenced my judgement and that code became increasingly obscured with each new cleaver idea I had until it was totally subjective. The word *obscured* comes from the Spanish word *oscuro* which means dark. My darkness didn't happen in one day or one deal, but was a process that built upon itself. It was not like I was a bad person. I was a good person who drifted off into my own interpretation of right and wrong, in part because I saw others doing the same thing and getting ahead by doing so.

I also learned that good people with good intensions can still cross the line. One of the people we helped at the clinic got convicted for what she did while trying to help others who had been defrauded by a dishonest businessman. She used half a million dollars of her own savings trying to save the investor's money, but needed time to turn the investment around and produced false financials to buy that time. When it was discovered she was arrested, convicted of financial crimes and sent to prison. Everything she had worked for in her entire adult life imploded along with her reputation and ability to do business when she got out, all in an effort to help others. It was a living example of wrong means cannot produce right results.

Before I open it up for your questions I want to impress upon you that there are many wonderful, caring, honest people like yourselves who never in a million years would think of crossing the moral, ethical, legal line, but when they unexpectedly find themselves in a situation they never encountered before, with their backs up against the wall, they become fearful and desperate. That fear and desperation triggers a fight or flight response and in a frantic need to survive they crossed the line. The only protection you have to lower the risk of finding yourself in a similar position is to reaffirm your values every day along with the belief that you have nothing to fear by sticking to them. If you do cross the line take responsibility for your actions, get back up and reaffirm your values again. Now I'll take any questions you may have."

Student: "You have probably been asked this question before, but did most of the people you met in prison take responsibility for their crimes?"

Susan Weinstock: "The short answer is no. Most of the people I met believed they were victims of the system; that what they did was something everybody does and they were just a scapegoat. I was one of them. It took me time to come to terms with what I had done and accept full responsibility for it. To me blame is counterproductive, it holds you down rather than propels you forward. Blame keeps you focused on the past and you have to let go of that to move forward. Some of those I met in prison were focused on seeking revenge against those they blamed for their incarceration and those who ratted them out to save their own skins. Holding on to this only perpetuates the punishment and prevents you from experiencing the best revenge of all that is, making something exemplary of your lives going forward."

Student: "Do most of the people who cross the line and get caught, cross it again?"

Susan Weinstock: "Some do, some do not. The ones who don't have come to terms with what they did, accept responsibility for it, recognize the part fear, greed, desperation, aggression, rule-bending and rationalization played in their decision making and realize they have to ditch their old ways of thinking and create newer healthier ways of dealing with problems."

Student: "What's the most common slippery slope that causes people to cross the line?"

Susan Weinstock: "In cases of white collar crime like mine the American culture has a lot to do with it and I'm not saying this in any way to excuse what I did. I take full responsibility for my actions and blame nobody but myself, but only mention it to point out that white-collar crime is often portrayed in the American culture as less a crime than a sibling of success. Rich powerful titans of Wall Street seldom get punished other than monetarily, save for the occasional ones you hear about. Also in the American culture being cleaver is often viewed as a positive especially if it creates great wealth for the perpetrator; the axiom being 'it's not wrong, it's just business.'"

Student: "If I understand what you are saying, the term 'white-collar crime' is a euphemism for a moral, ethical breach committed by a person of high social status rather than a person of a lower class unless that lower class person has made a lot of money?"

Susan Weinstock: "Yes, there seems to be some political/social justifications for this viewpoint. Of course the obvious being that people with money and power tend be held in high esteem and have access to other people in power and the best lawyers who can concoct effective defenses. And too, that prosecutors, government officials and others involved in the judicial system realize that punishing people with money and power could have a ripple effect on their own political life such as shutting down a source of contributions or a city or state's major source of employment or the damage it might do to a high ranking official like the scandal at Enron and its connection to President Bush and his family. While some of the Enron people were convicted they were also quietly let out of jail, the same with those at the top who were convicted in the big Savings and Loan scandal. It's of note that *CFO Magazine* has quietly abandoned its annual Excellence Awards, because the winners from each of the previous three years had gone to prison."

Student: "I read that since 2000 the prosecution of white-collar crime has plummeted."

Susan Weinstock: "Yes, but this should not imply a surge in moralism among our leading capitalists. After the attacks of September 11th, the F.B.I. began to shift resources toward counterterrorism and away from white collar crime. Meanwhile, lawmakers cut the budget of the Internal Revenue Service so sharply that it has the same number of special agents in 2017 as it had half a century earlier even though the national population has grown by two-thirds."

Student: "I read an article and we talked about it in class where the Department of Justice claimed, as you said, it is difficult prove fraudulent intent by Wall Street executives who are many layers removed from the crimes committed by their companies. Critics have labeled it 'willfully blind' and that resolution has more to do with fines and sometimes compensating victims than punishing those responsible, thus there's no deterrent to committing more crimes."

Susan Weinstock: "Yes, exactly. In addition, many convicted criminals attribute their crimes to a kind of societal inadequacy; not being able to tell their families they can't afford a certain life style. Then there's the uncomfortable question about some of America's most suspect businesses, are they attracting rogues or grooming them? Eugene Soltes a professor at Harvard Business School, reportedly said that regulations are partly to blame declaring, 'There is more white-collar crime today because there are more things that are criminal today than fifty years ago. Bribing a foreign official for instance was legal until the Foreign Corrupt Practices Act of 1977, and insider trading was rarely prosecuted until the nineteen-eighties. Today, those are among the most common offenses.' But I view these comments more as an excuse to blame others for a breach in morals and ethics than a contributing factor. There was no shortage of excuses in prison to blame others or the system for crossing the line. When you knowingly break the law or violate society's code of morals and ethics you only have yourself to blame. What is interesting too, is what Soltes learned when he interviewed scores of people convicted or accused of white-collar crime. It was something he called 'psychological distance' between perpetrators and their victims: Business is done with individuals at greater length now, which reduces the feeling that managers are harming others. People agree to sacrifice the life of someone they can't see far more readily than that of someone who stands before them.' It's similar to what soldiers face in war where the enemy is reduced to an object rather than a human being making it easier for the soldier to kill them."

Professor Meyer: "Susan if I might, I would like to interject some thoughts on that very concept. Philosopher Aldous Huxley in his essay on the Industrial Revolution postured that as society moved away from direct connection with one another as in face to face contact, the distance would result in a dysphoria that would be harmful to our morals and ethics. As a soldier in Vietnam I recognized exactly what you said about dehumanizing the other side. The military went to great lengths to label the enemy with colloquial terms like, 'Charlie', Gooks, Sloops, targets and objectives, thus making killing them much easier because psychologically we were not killing people. Once we lose sight of our unity with each other we can be manipulated into doing anything and justifying it."

Susan Weinstock: "Thank you professor, that's so true. What Soltes and others have said, 'In recent years, the lament that moral constraints have weakened, has been voiced not just by critics of Wall Street, but by practitioners.

In 2012, John C. Bogle, the iconic investor who founded the Vanguard Group and spent more than six decades in finance, wrote, 'When I came into this field, the standard seemed to be 'there are some things that one simply doesn't do.' Today, the standard is 'if everyone else is doing it, I can do it too.' Soon afterward, the law firm Labaton Sucharow conducted a survey of finance professionals in which a quarter of them said that they would engage in insider trading to make ten million dollars if they could get away with it. Around the same time, Greg Smith, an executive director at Goldman Sachs, announced his resignation, decrying 'a decline in the firm's moral fiber.' Writing in the *Times*, he observed, 'Over the last 12 months I have seen five different managing directors refer to their own clients as 'Muppets.' You don't have to be a rocket scientist to figure out that the junior analyst sitting quietly in the corner of the room hearing about 'Muppets,' 'ripping eyeballs out' and 'getting paid' doesn't exactly turn into a model citizen.'

Researchers have elucidated on the way that dubious behavior moves through a community. 'In the period between 2000 and 2009 the federal government brought several criminal and civil cases for backdating stock options—manipulating records so that executives could take home a larger return than their options really delivered. Studies found that the practice had started in Silicon Valley and then infected the broader business world. The vectors of transmission could be traced to specific individuals who served as directors or auditors of multiple companies. An unethical habit spreads in encounters among neighbors and colleagues through subtle cues that psychologists call *affective evaluations.* If people are rising on one measurement profit, even as they are falling on another ethics, the verdict about which matters more will hinge on the culture around them—on which values are most exalted by members of their insular business communities. Concluding, 'If you spend time with people who pick locks, you will probably learn to pick locks.'

In 2013, prosecutors announced an indictment of S.A.C. Capital Advisors—named for its founder, Steven A. Cohen—calling it a 'veritable magnet for market cheaters.' Cohen, like a considerable number of his peers, lived in Greenwich, Connecticut. In the previous decade, as the hedge-fund industry surged in scale and profits, the rise of the Internet had allowed funds to leave Wall Street and many moved to southern Connecticut to take advantage of favorable tax rates and easy commutes. By 2005, hedge funds had taken over two-thirds of Greenwich's commercial real estate.

After the charges against Cohen were announced, David Rafferty, a columnist for Greenwich *Time*, a local paper, published a piece with the headline 'GREENWICH, GATEWAY TO WHITE-COLLAR CRIME.' He wrote, 'A few years ago you might have been proud to tell your friends you lived in 'The Hedge Fund Capital of the World.' Now? Not so much.'

Rafferty, in his column, described a 'growing sense of unease in certain circles as one hedgie after another seemed to be facing the music.' Cohen, however, faced the music for a limited interlude. Under an agreement brokered with prosecutors, his firm pleaded guilty to insider trading and was sentenced to pay $1.8 billion in penalties. After a two-year suspension, Cohen returned to the hedge-fund business, and made enough money to buy the New York Mets. The price was $2.4 billion, the largest sum ever paid for a North American sports franchise.

Luigi Zingales, a finance professor at the University of Chicago, reportedly said that he wishes his profession spoke more candidly about accountability and impunity. Most of the time business schools find every possible way to avoid the moral questions. I don't know of any alum who has been kicked out of the alumni association for immoral behavior. There are trustees of business schools today who have been convicted of bribery and insider trading, and I don't think people notice or care. He reportedly went on to say, 'People are getting more and more comfortable in the gray area.'

Not long after graduating from business school at Wharton, Tom Hardin or, as he is known with some notoriety in Wall Street circles, Tipper X, went to work for a hedge fund in Greenwich. He had much to learn. Almost instantly, he began hearing that some competitors, such as the billionaire <u>Raj Rajaratnam</u>, were suspected of relying on illegal tips from company insiders; Rajaratnam was later convicted and sentenced to eleven years. In 2007, after Hardin became a partner at Lanexa Global Management, a hedge fund in New York, he got his own inside tip, a heads-up on an upcoming acquisition and he traded on the information and beat the market. He repeated similar stunts three times. He reportedly said, 'I'm, like, I would never get caught if I buy a small amount of stock, this is like dropping a penny in the Grand Canyon. You can say, I'm highly ethical and would never do this. But once you're in the environment and you feel like everybody else is doing it and you feel you're not hurting anybody, it's very easy to convince yourself.'

In 2008, Hardin was walking out of the dry cleaner's when two F.B.I. agents approached him. They sat him down in a Wendy's nearby and told him that they knew about his illegal trades. He had a choice, go to jail or wear a wire. He chose the latter and became one of the most productive informants in the history of securities fraud. The F.B.I. gave him a tiny recorder disguised as a cell-phone battery which he slipped into his shirt pocket to gather evidence in more than twenty criminal cases brought under *Operation Perfect Hedge*. For a year and a half his identity was disguised in court documents as Tipper X, fueling a mystery around what the *Times* called 'the secret witness at the center of the biggest insider-trading case in a generation.'

In December, 2009, Hardin pleaded guilty and his identity was revealed in court filings. He had avoided prison but become a felon, which made features of a normal life all but impossible, from opening a brokerage account to coaching his daughters' soccer team. He was unsure how he could earn a living. 'I would ask my attorney, are there any past clients you can connect me with who've got to the other side of this and are back on their feet?' He was, like, 'Sorry, not really.'

In his dealings with his peers, Hardin has learned to distinguish who is genuinely remorseful from who is not.

'I'll hear from white-collar felons who tell me, 'I made a mistake. I'll say, 'A mistake is something we do without intention. A bad *decision* was made intentionally.' If you're classifying your bad decisions as mistakes, you're not accepting responsibility.'

Professor Meyer: "Susan I could listen to you for hours to come, but unfortunately the clock says we've out of time. Let's thank Susan for her outstanding presentation."

Following applause.

Susan Weinstock: "Thank you, it's been my pleasure and honor to have this opportunity to be with you. I hope you found what I said to be of value and wish you all the best in your lives and careers."

Following Susan Weinstock's departure.

Professor Meyer: "I'll leave you with two of my favorite quotes on the subject of ethics and morality.
    As a one-time student of existentialist philosophy I liked this quote from French author, philosopher Albert Camus on ethics, 'A man without ethics is a wild beast loosed upon this world.' And this one from physicist and Nobel Laureate, Albert Einstein on morality, 'The most important human endeavor is the striving for morality in our actions. Our inner balance and even our very existence depend on it. Only morality in our actions can give beauty and dignity to life.'

I look forward to seeing you all next week when we continue the conversation with Thoughts on Morals and Ethics in Business. Don't' forget the reading Assignments for Class Six in *Small is Beautiful* and *The Compassionate Universe.* Class dismissed.

CLASS SIX

THOUGHTS ON MORALS AND ETHICS IN BUSINESS

Professor Meyer: "Welcome back it's good to see you again. Today we are going to continue our discussion on moral and ethical issues with emphasis on businesses, especially corporations. Here's some insightful commentary about corporations, found on the Internet.

'What makes corporations different from individually owned and unincorporated businesses is their special status. They are legal entities that are separate from their owners. They can make a profit, be taxed and held legally liable, but their owners the shareholders, cannot. Corporations offer the strongest protection to owners from personal liability. As such a corporation can act with impunity without its owners and in many cases its employees and managers being held accountable.

Even if you have the best idea and the most committed employees, maintaining a successful business is going to be an everyday challenge. It's not uncommon for companies large and small alike to feel this pressure and wonder if there isn't an easier way. Some may decide to work harder, whereas others turn to unethical business practices.

These unethical business practices encompasses anything that falls below widely accepted minimum standards for a business code of conduct. This includes any behaviors that are generally viewed as morally and ethically wrong and lead to the mistreatment of people, animals, or the environment.

In general, businesses have found countless ways to act unethically. Most of these actions fall into four main categories: Unethical practices toward customers, unethical practices toward employees, unfair competition and legal, but unethical practices. Some examples of actual unethical business practices are:

Exploiting workers.
Over-billing customers.
Exploiting tax loopholes.
Polluting the environment; dumping toxins into the air or water.
Prescribing unnecessary medical procedures.
Covering up defects.
Designing phones so that users accidentally accept data charges.

Creating fake identities.
False Product Claims.
Hidden Terms in User Agreements.
Unethical Accounting.
Poor Working Conditions.
Sexual Harassment.
Defamation.
Trade Secret Misappropriation.
Bribery.

Unethical businesses use methods that target customers and hope consumers will fail to notice they're being tricked. They rely on the fact that they'll be able to make numerous sales without the word spreading that they're being deceptive. For example: False Product Claims. There's a huge difference between using marketing to paint a product or service in the best possible light and outright lying. With traditional advertising, companies use misleading language to target customers and with digital advertising it's even easier, because there's minimal oversight.

To back up the claims they make in their ads, companies may use fake reviews or ask influencers to endorse their products; although many platforms are cracking down on fake reviews by requiring posts from influencers to specify that the posts are promotional. In addition some platforms have begun to monitor ads more closely. However, you might notice that required disclosures are in such small print they are de facto unreadable or if on television disappear before they can be read.

Hidden Terms in User Agreements. Every time you sign up for a new service or download software (including free software), you need to click the 'Agree' button on the user agreement. Almost no one reads these pages-long user agreements, which can enable businesses to slip in some undesirable requirements. For instance, you may be allowing a company to sell your data to a third party or you could be giving a social media platform the rights to your content. Companies can put anything they want into these terms of service, including requirements that are not actually legal or are unenforceable.

Unethical Accounting. Intentionally mismanaging accounts can make a company seem more profitable than it really is. This hurts investors who may purchase shares in the company only to end up losing when the truth is revealed.

Unethical Business Practices towards Employees. Another way for businesses to get ahead unethically is by treating employees unfairly; this can keep costs down and improve productivity.

Poor Working Conditions. Low-wage workers are often subject to long hours and may be refused overtime with the threat of being fired if they don't comply. During the pandemic, the number of employees forced to work in unsafe conditions has also risen. For instance, workers may lack personal protective equipment or be unable to maintain social distancing. The situation is even worse for undocumented workers, as well as immigrants with work visas who worry they will lose their permits if they complain. Unethical companies may also take advantage of the more lax regulations in developing countries and outsource manufacturing jobs or other work to benefit from cheap labor.

Sexual Harassment. Companies sometimes dismiss employee reports of sexual harassment or use gag orders to keep cases out of public knowledge which often allows abuse to continue unchecked. In other cases, sexual abuse could come from the very top. The *MeToo* movement has shown just how pervasive sexual harassment and abuse is in the business world. Even false accusations and public perception can ruin and/or end careers; this causes some men to refuse to mentor women.' Here at GRU I was sent to one of our remote campuses to have a window installed in the office door of the director who some students claimed was a little to fatherly in hugging them.

'The problem is we live in an economic system premised on inequality and exploitation. Our society is a well-known pyramid with those at the very top enjoying comforts and privileges most at the bottom will never know in their lifetimes. That small number of people making up the capstone have grown accustomed to not living like the rest. For some, this singularity resembles exceptionalism; and if you're not like the rest, why would the law apply to you like it applies to everybody else? The disintegration of morality and empathy in those with access to inordinate power or wealth has long been the subject of cultural exploration. So it seems somewhat perplexing that there are still those who can't fathom how the rich and famous could ever become abusers. Abuse can happen anywhere, to nearly anyone. But it is unsurprising that it is so frequently wielded by the most powerful in our society. To be sure, not all wealthy people are abusers, and not all have lost their capacity for compassion, respect and solidarity.

Unfair Competition. One of the biggest threats to any business is its competitors. Some companies try to give themselves an unfair advantage by attacking their competition through a few different types of unethical business practices. For example, defamation. In the digital era it's easier than ever to spread false information. Businesses can create fake accounts on social media or post anonymously on blogs or forums to spread lies about a competitor. If the identity of the user is discovered, the business may receive a hefty fine.

Trade Secret Misappropriation. Trade secret infringement can be intentional or due to negligence. In either case, it can provide a company with information that gives it an unfair economic advantage.

Bribery. Businesses may bribe government officials or industry leaders to secure better deals or gain a foothold in the market. The company may offer money or something else of value, such as political support or better deals on its products and services.

Legal but unethical business practices. There are some unethical business practices that are legal but morally questionable. There's nothing to stop businesses partaking in these activities, especially if they think that their products and services are desirable enough that customers will continue to purchase them anyway.

Selling Customer Data. As noted before, companies may include the right to sell customer data in their agreement terms. Often, this is completely legal, especially if the data contains no personally-identifiable information. Usually, companies sell this data to advertisers or startups who want a database they can market to.

Complex Securities. By making investment structures so complex that even experts struggle to decipher them, companies are able to swindle investors while staying within the law. Examples of unethical business practices like this include credit default swaps, mortgage-backed securities, hedge funds, and special investment vehicles. Typically, the company offering the investment understates the risk, but the risk becomes apparent later when the portfolio or pension plan funds sink.

What Are the Consequences of Unethical Business Practices? The consequences of practicing unethical business depends on two main factors: was the practice illegal and was the business caught? If the unethical practice was against the law, the business may suffer a fine — sometimes in the millions of dollars. And sometimes, those responsible for the action will receive prison time. Of course, if the practice is never detected or cannot be proven, it's not possible to take legal action against the company. However, if consumers suspect wrongdoing, they may demand changes from the business or start a boycott.

Here are some well-known examples of unethical business practices by well-known corporations found on the Internet.

Wells Fargo. In 1981, the bank was involved in one of the largest embezzlements in history. Then, with its shady mortgage practices, the company became a major player in the 2008 financial crisis. Shortly after, to help the business recover, Wells Fargo pressured employees to set up hidden accounts in customers' names. This continued until the scheme's discovery in 2016.

Ferrero USA. Ferrero USA is the company behind the brand Nutella. It was forced to pay a settlement of $3.05 million after settling a class action lawsuit for falsely advertising that its chocolate spread is a nutritious choice for children.

Volkswagen. Almost everyone is familiar with one of the latest cases of corporate misconduct: the Volkswagen emissions scandal. The company admitted to having installed software that manipulated emissions readings to make its cars appear as if they were environmentally friendly.

Foxconn. For years, Foxconn has been accused of violating labor rights. Recent leaks revealed that the company employs children as young as 14 years old to work in its factories in China. The supplier provides products to both Apple and Amazon.

Coca Cola. Back in 2009, Coca-Cola promoted *PowerAde* as having more electrolytes than *Gatorade,* the rival energy drink from Pepsi. In retaliation Pepsi sued Coca-Cola on the grounds that its claim had no basis in science.

Since the 1990s Coca-Cola has been accused of unethical behavior in a number of areas, including product safety, anti-competitiveness, racial discrimination, channel stuffing, distributor conflicts, intimidation of union workers, pollution, depletion of natural resources, and health concerns.

Halliburton. One of the largest oil companies in the world, Halliburton has been accused of a number of grave offenses. These include doing business with countries with which the US government has banned trade relations, over-charging the US army for supplies during the Iraq War in 2003, mismanaging waste, sexual assault, and exposing employees to hazardous chemicals.

The internet, and particularly social media, have given consumers a greater voice. Many people are choosing to speak out about what they consider to be unethical business practices. This can cause severe damage to a company's image and damage brand loyalty. Consumers also understand that money speaks — that they have the purchasing power to buy from businesses they consider ethical.

Whereas we are still far from seeing an end to unethical behaviors, consumers' actions are slowly making more of an impact. Plus, businesses now have a new way to beat the competition: show that they are the moral choice by engaging in ethical business practices.

McDonald's. Fast-food giant McDonald's has been named the most unethical firm in the world because of its business conduct, including the way it treats its suppliers. The firm was ranked least ethical in an index compiled by the Fraser Consultancy, which assessed 42 brands from sectors ranging from food to fashion.

Nestle. Nestle aggressively pushed their breastfeeding formula in less economically developed countries specifically targeting the poor. They made it seem that their infant formula was almost as good as a mother's milk, which is highly unethical for several reasons.'

Here's a category list found on the Internet of Nestlé's allegedly unethical practices. Let me remind you that these are alleged and are presented not necessarily as truths, but to educate by provoking thought: 'Baby Formula and Boycott; Nestle and Water; Child labor abuse and trafficking; Health Threats; Pollution; Ethiopian Debt; A personal deal with president Mugabe of Zimbabwe; Price Fixing; Promoting Unhealthy Food and Mislabeling.

Amazon. Amazon is an arch tax avoider and is the subject of a global boycott called by the Ethical Consumer. The world's biggest online retailer is generating huge revenues in the UK, but paying very little corporation tax. It does this by funneling money through its holding company in the notorious tax haven of Luxembourg.'

Some of these breaches are minor compared to those we will explore later when we review the documentary entitled '*The Corporation.*' For now however, I would like you to consider the following career opportunity:

Post-graduation you receive a job offer to be the executive in charge of marketing for a leading cigarette manufacturing company. Your territory, the continent of Africa. Beside an excellent six figure starting salary there are numerous perks, you will be headquartered in a country where the cost of living is considerably less than in the US so your money will go a lot further enabling you to live like a multi-millionaire at the top echelon of society with a nice home, a staff of servants and a luxury car. Your primary job responsibility will be to increase the sales of cigarettes among one of the least educated vulnerable populations in the world. It should be easy because the product is highly addictive yet detrimental to the consumer's health and many will suffer and die from it. By a show of hands, how many of you would take the job? Honest answers only and no judgment."

Only one hand goes up.

Professor Meyer: "Why would you take the job knowing the harm the product will cause others?"

Student: Because it's a great job and if I don't take it someone else will. It's not like I will be changing anything."

Professor Meyer: "Thank you for your honesty. How many of you who did not raise your hands did so because of the moral and ethical issues involved?

All other hands go up.

Professor Meyer: "Many of the hardest decisions we will ever make center on moral and ethical issues. For example in a news article written by Murray Fromson a professor of journalism at USC he discussed the actions Bob Kerrey former senator, governor and would be presidential candidate. According to the Article, Kerrey along with members of his Navy Seal Team, allegedly participated in an action during the Vietnam War in which elderly, civilian men and women, along with children, including infants, were killed by the Seal Team either by having their throats cut or bodies torn apart by automatic weapons. Having served in Vietnam I'll assume they did so believing they were carrying out their patriotic duty in vanquishing our Country's enemy notwithstanding the fact that such acts are an atrocity and designated as a war crime.

Another such incident was noted in the article wherein a Marine corporal whose commanding officer was going to nominate him for a Silver Star, our nation's second-highest medal for heroism, for an action he took days before participating in the broad daylight torturing, dismembering and summarily executing of two unarmed Vietnamese peasant rice farmers whose only crime was wearing black pajamas which he and his follow soldiers took to mean they were Viet Cong. The article detailed that one farmer had been hanged and before dying, his throat was slashed and his heart was cut open. The article further described the young Marine squad leader as a good looking shy kid of 20 and son of a Pentecostal minister from a mid-western town. It is difficult if not impossible for us to put ourselves in the shoes of these men in those moments because of the element of war. In Bob Kerrey's situation there were questions about the village supporting the enemy and in that of the young Marine, they supposedly had recently discovered the body of their former platoon leader who had been executed with his hands bound by barbed wire, his penis cut off and stuffed in his mouth. It's very likely due to those circumstances, that in both cases once the killing began adrenaline likely overwhelmed rational thought. A quote in the article also touched on a mindset in war culture 'We were there to kill the Cong, the enemy, and to do that you had to teach our men to hate the people.' Let me ask you this, by a show of hands, how many of you could see yourselves slitting the throats of elderly men and women or an infant in such a situation? Before you answer I want you to understand that I am not talking about pointing a gun and pulling the trigger an act that is somewhat remote and somewhat impersonal, but holding a baby or grandmother with one hand and slitting their throats with the other."

No hands go up.

Professor Meyer: "The point I'm trying to make is that you will likely be exposed in your personal and/or professional lives to a culture that through subtle and/or overt conditioning will pressure you to cross a moral and/or ethical threshold that you would otherwise never do and you need to prepare yourself to recognize this before it over takes you and you find yourself going along with the crowd. Many companies proclaim their moral and ethical culture in their mission statement and HR guidelines even posting it on their letterhead and on the walls of their offices, yet their real culture is very different and you might be pressured or tempted to go along with the herd out of self-preservation and/or protecting the organization as being more important than doing the right thing.

Will you have the strength to be the odd person out, versus playing the game? To walk away from the security of a great job and the friendship of your co-workers if need be, instead of rationalizing along with others as to why you shouldn't walk away? In last week's class you heard how one person crossed the line because she saw a moral duty to protect investor's money and save the company. No doubt in your own personal and professional lives there will be situations involving moral and ethical principles versus loyalty to others, how are you going to prepare yourself to deal with them? What will guide you in the process?

Having never been in a war or perhaps a similar situation your answers will likely be hypothetical, but here's a situation you might encounter and one closer to home. As you know GRU strongly underscores its Christian values in addition to academia. Not too long ago it received a significant gift of many millions of dollars from a longtime friend of one of its key employees who had recommended to his friend that instead of leaving his estate to him personally, that his friend gift it to GRU so that it would help prepare students for a life of purpose as fundamental to GRU's moral and ethical standards. His friend took this advice and donated the bulk of his estate to GRU, but included a small gift to his friend who had taken care of him for over twenty years, and a few smaller gifts to other charitable organizations. In documenting the gift, two of the university's advancement employees one of them a university employee attorney, visited the donor without the friend being present to ensure there was no untold influence to include the employee in the donor's estate. Subsequently GRU's in-house lawyer prepared the gift documents and had the donor execute them. When the donor died, the donor's brother hired a lawyer and challenged the gift based on a State law that required the University's lawyer as both the drafter of the documents on behalf of GRU, and GRU being a recipient of the gift, to advise the donor in writing, that he should consult a third party neutral lawyer to insure that the bequest complied with his wishes and there was no undue influence. While the law exempted a well-recognized nonprofit like GRU the employee who brought the gift to GRU was not, which meant the employee's gift was in jeopardy. However the law permitted the employee to sue GRU on behalf of the deceased donor for failing to properly advise him as required by law and thus putting the donor's wishes in jeopardy. Under the statute, the penalty for the GRU lawyer who failed to advise the donor of this legal requirement could have led to the lawyer's disbarment. Caught off guard and in defense, GRU's legal department told the employee although he was a long time well respected and valued employee and a good friend who had brought many such gifts to GRU, they could not represent his interest in the lawsuit due to a conflict of interest, but that GRU would give him five thousand dollars toward covering his legal expenses, then handed him an envelope saying all the details were in a letter. When the employee read the letter it stated that in order to get the five thousand dollars which did not even cover the initial retainer for the employee's lawyer, it required that the employee sign a declaration stating the university's lawyer who drafted the gift documents did so on his own and not as an employee of GRU; this notwithstanding the fact that GRU's full-time attorney employee and the other employee did so by direction of GRU, on GRU's time and payroll and were even reimbursed for their trip expenses. In other words, GRU's legal department wanted to protect GRU with a lie even if that meant the GRU lawyer could lose his license to practice law. The employee never signed the document and never received the five thousand dollars or any financial assistance not withstanding it was solely through that employee's unselfish efforts that GRU was enriched by more than twelve million dollars. In addition GRU deliberately conspired to put the procuring employee's gift in jeopardy by refusing to sign a tolling agreement which would have put the statute of limitations for the employee to sue GRU on hold while they tried to work things out; only relenting at the eleventh hour of the last day despite the employees many request to do so; then lied to the employee about it by saying they didn't know about his request. The point of retelling this story is that GRU's leadership deliberately set aside their Christian code of morals and ethics which would have compelled them to honesty and fair dealing with the situation. Instead they took the position that protecting themselves and GRU from the consequences of their error was more important, notwithstanding the harm to others."

Student: "That's terrible. How did it end up?"

Professor Meyer: "The case was turned over to GRU's outside counsel and ultimately settled out of court, but not without considerable cost to GRU, the employee who procured the gift, the lawyer who drafted the documents and outside beneficiaries of the estate. The employee lawyer later resigned due to GRU's willingness to throw him under the bus to save face and the legal department blamed all the unfair dealing on their outside legal counsel saying "oh you know, it's the lawyers" as if the University had no say over how the case was being handled. What would you do if an employer instructed you to take a similar stance, one that you knew to be untruthful and unethical, in order to protect the company?"

Student: "I assume the in-house lawyers felt their jobs were in jeopardy if they didn't do what they were told to do by their bosses. Isn't this the real question?"

Professor Meyer: "In part yes. It was systemic and went down the chain of command. So what would you do?"

Student: "I honestly don't know. I want to say I would have refuse because it was unethical, but then I might be out of a job and how would I pay my bills or how would getting fired affect my chances of getting another job? And even if they didn't fire me my chances of getting promoted or getting a raise would likely be compromised. It's easier for me to answer this in a vacuum by saying I would refuse to do so for moral and ethical reasons, but in real life that might not be the case. So how would you answer this professor?"

Professor Meyer: "To your point, there's a difference between intellectual knowledge and wisdom; for example the doctor who smokes even though he knows it's detrimental to his health. And a difference between hypothetical and real situations. Another alternative to getting fired would be to resign. In reflection I would have to say at different times of my life I likely would have handled it differently. That's what growing and learning is about and what Gandhi meant when he responded to a reporter's question about his years ago activities that contrasted with his current position, by saying 'that's who I was then.' Today, I am confident that I would have had a friendly talk with leadership about how the morals and ethics of the University can only be expressed by its actions and that I personally affiliated myself with the University because of those values and cannot bring myself to violate them. I would have reminded leadership too, that wrong actions can never lead to right results and we can't escape the consequences of those actions. I would like to believe that this would have caused leadership to reconsider its position, but I can't be sure."

Student: "And if they didn't, what would you have done?"

Professor Meyer: "I would have refused to be a part of it and suffered the consequence of my decision. Likely they would have let me resign rather than fire me. But then, I am in a much better emotional and financial position today to bear those consequences than I was when I was your age fresh out of college and just starting my career. Then again, when I was your age, single and responsible only for myself, I might have refused to be a part of the unethical deportment. It seems the mid-career period when there's more responsibility to others is where such a decision gets more challenging and that is exactly why we are having this discussion."

Student: "So when you were our age would you have supported GRU's position?"

Professor Meyer: "In hind sight knowing what I now know about morals and ethics, definitely not. I am committed to honesty and fair dealing and know that wrong means can never lead to right results and what I do to others I do to myself. Easwaran said it best, "We chose our own destiny, because consequences are a part of every action."

Student: "So did the University suffer adverse consequences for their actions?"

Professor Meyer: "Absolutely. As we discussed, once you cross the ethical line it becomes obfuscated and you are floating around in a space without defined borders. While the majority of the University's employees and supporters never knew of the incident and some only after the fact, the culture definitely changed from a close secure working family held to together by common values, to one of insecurity where employees did not feel they or their efforts were valued, only their fidelity to leadership. As I said, the lawyer who drafted the gift agreement quit his job and went to work for another organization and the employee who was wronged never felt the same about GRU. He lost his zeal for approaching other prospective donors. Even the lawyers in GRU legal office were not the same. I sensed they felt ashamed for what they had done to a undeserving colleague and realized it could have been them on the other end of the situation and might be one day in the future. Once the line is crossed it's a moving target.

Student: "Are you saying GRU is in trouble of losing its Christian culture?"

Professor Meyer: "To my way seeing, GRU has already miscarried its Christian values and is free floating and there's no telling where it's going to land. Hopefully it will regain them, but I don't see that happening anytime in the near future as those traditional values have morphed into a new base; a new line in the sand which has given way to an undercurrent meme to wit, 'the founders of GRU had vision and values, but no money, the current leaders have money and no vision.' As to failing as a viable business and academic enterprise, only time will tell. As to regaining its Christian values I think of Harvard College which was founded by Puritans as a Christian school and later named for Rev. John Harvard. It has long since been secular. And many other colleges and universities that were founded on Christian values have long since abandoned that path.

Consider that in handing this or any such situation it does not have to be a zero sum approach. There are pragmatic and ethical ways to come together and resolve conflict. For example, GRU could have admitted the error, after all humans make errors, and negotiated with the brother for a financial settlement, which in an early mediation they flatly refused to do. But in the end it was exactly what happened only they did so after spending hundreds of thousands of dollars in legal fees and alienating not only the two loyal employees and the donor's friends who found out about it, but those other employees who heard what happened. As a result the donor's friends openly took GRU out of their Wills and convinced others to do the same, and worse as I said, GRU's employee culture and morale suffered. You either stand for something or you stand for nothing. This leads me to the issue about how some religious leaders and followers often substitute dogma for wisdom. They may declare that they follow Jehovah or Jesus or Mohammed, but they fail to follow their teachings of fair dealing, kindness, inclusion and non-judgment, instead requiring those things of others rather than themselves; exactly the opposite of what their founders stood for. As such these leaders and sometimes their followers became the infidels, the heathen, the heretics mentioned in their scripture. As Gandhi declared 'make of yourselves the world as you want it to be.' Not make others bend to your professed beliefs. A true Christian, Jew, Muslim etc. can easily be identified by how they conduct themselves as in 'your belief is only as deep as your actions.' Religious training and fidelity are about working on yourself not on others.

Intrinsically you know the right thing to do, it is only fear that causes you to question it. You must always ask yourself will this decision take me closer to my goal or further away from it, and remember that only right actions can lead to right results.

Now is a good time for us to segue into a report from the team assigned to review the documentary *"Enron: The Smartest Guys in the Room."*

Student: "The documentary examines the 2001 collapse of the Enron Corporation and subsequent criminal trials for several of the company's top executives. It was adapted from a book written by Bethany McLean and Peter Elkind, first published in 2003 called *The Amazing Rise and Scandalous Fall of Enron* that explored the fall of the Enron Corporation, arguably the most shocking example of modern corporate corruption. The company was linked to several illegal schemes, including instigating the California energy crisis as a way to drive up utility prices at the expense of the average American. In a hyper-competitive environment, Enron traders resorted to underhanded dealings in order to make money at any cost and keep their high-paying jobs. I highly recommend the book and documentary as a case study in corporate greed and malfeasance."

Student: To continue, the documentary covers the president of Enron Kenneth Ley who founded the company after cultivating a strong relationship with future presidents George H.W. Bush and George W. Bush. When oil traders began betting on the oil markets the company fell under suspicion for reporting high profits and diverting company money to personal off shore accounts. When auditors discovered this, Kenneth Lay encouraged them to continue the deception of Enron making millions on the books that wasn't there in fact the companies traders were fired when it was discovered that they had gambled away Enron's reserves and the company was essentially bankrupt. Lay denied having any knowledge of this although it was likely he orchestrated it or at least turn a blind eye to the practice."

Student: "At one point Lay knew that one of the company's divisions had two sets of books, one for the company and one for the traders themselves and that they were stealing from the company, but he also knew it was the only division making money so he let them continue. Lay hired a new CEO named Jeffrey Skilling on the condition they utilize market to market accounting which allowed the company to book potential profits when the deals were signed even if those projects later lost money."

Student: "And then there was Lou Pai the CEO of Enron Energy Services who was obsessed with strippers and used Company funds to hire them. He ultimately retired from the company and sold his stock for two hundred and fifty million dollars having covered up the fact that his division had lost a billion dollars. He then divorced his wife and married a stripper. Lay and Skillings attempted to hide the losses, pump up the stock prices with fraudulent claims, and then dump their own holdings of the stock."

Student: "At budget meetings, Skilling would develop target earnings by asking, "What earnings do you need to keep our stock price up?" and that number would be used, even if it was not feasible. Using Enron's January 2001 stock price of $83.13 and the directors beneficial ownership reported in the 2001 proxy, the value of director stock ownership, was $659 million for Lay, and $174 million for Skilling.

Skilling believed that if Enron employees were constantly worried about cost, it would hinder original thinking. As a result, extravagant spending was rampant throughout the company, especially among the executives. Employees had large expense accounts and many executives were paid sometimes twice as much as competitors. In 1998, the top 200 highest-paid employees received $193 million from salaries, bonuses, and stock. Two years later, the figure jumped to $1.4 billion"

Student: "By using accounting loopholes and poor financial reporting they were able to hide billions of dollars in debt from failed deals and projects. Chief Financial Officer Andrew Fastow and other executives misled Enron›s board of directors and audit committee on high-risk accounting practices and pressured Arthur Andersen to ignore the issues. The company declared bankruptcy and its accounting firm, Arthur Andersen, then one of the five largest audit and accountancy partnerships in the world was effectively dissolved. In addition to being the largest bankruptcy reorganization in U.S. history at that time, Enron was cited as the biggest audit failure.

Enron shareholders filed a $40 billion lawsuit after the company's stock price, which achieved a high of US $90.75 per share in mid-2000, plummeted to less than $1 by the end of November 2001."

Many executives at Enron were indicted for a variety of charges and some were later sentenced to prison, including Lay and Skilling. Arthur Andersen was found guilty of illegally destroying documents relevant to the SEC investigation, which voided its license to audit public companies and effectively closed the firm. By the time the ruling was overturned at the U.S. Supreme Court Arthur Andersen had lost the majority of its customers and had ceased operating. Enron employees and shareholders received limited returns in lawsuits, despite losing billions in pensions and stock prices.

Fastow and his wife, Lea, both plead guilty to charges against them. Fastow was initially charged with 98 counts of fraud, money laundering, insider trading and conspiracy, among other crimes. Fastow plead guilty to two charges of conspiracy and was sentenced to ten years with no parole in a plea bargain to testify against Lay, Skilling, and Causey. Lea was indicted on six felony counts, but prosecutors later dismissed them in favor of a single misdemeanor tax charge. Lea was sentenced to one year for helping her husband hide income from the government.

Lay and Skilling went on trial for their part in the Enron scandal in January 2006. The 53-count, 65-page indictment covers a broad range of financial crimes, including bank fraud, making false statements to banks and auditors, securities fraud, wire fraud, money laundering, conspiracy, and insider trading. On May 25, 2006, the jury in the Lay and Skilling trial returned its verdicts. Skilling was convicted of 19 of 28 counts of securities fraud and wire fraud and acquitted on the remaining nine, including charges of insider trading. He was sentenced to 24 years and 4 months in prison. In 2013 the United States Department of Justice reached a deal with Skilling, which resulted in ten years being cut from his sentence.

Lay pleaded not guilty to the eleven criminal charges and claimed that he was misled by those around him. He attributed the main cause for the company's demise to Fastow. Lay was convicted of all six counts of securities and wire fraud for which he had been tried, and he was subjected to a maximum total sentence of 45 years in prison. However, before sentencing was scheduled, Lay died on July 5, 2006.

At the time of his death, the SEC had been seeking more than $90 million from Lay in addition to civil fines.

Professor Meyer: "Thank you for that report. Are there any questions or comments?"

Student: "Did anything ever happen to the Bushes'?"

Professor Meyer: "In a New York Times article at the time, it said that President H.W. Bush was trying to distance himself from Enron and play down his relationship with its chairman Kenneth Lay, but 'their ties are broad and deep and go back many years and that the relationship had been beneficial to both.' The article also quoted Craig McDonald, director of Texans for Public Justice, as saying, "President Bush's explanation of his relationship to Enron is at best a half truth. He was in bed with Enron before he ever held a political office.'

As to the younger president Bush, the article said that Kenneith Lay and Bush had developed a warm relationship with each other when Bush was governor of Texas and that Bush had done favors for Lay such as calling the governor of Pennsylvania to vouch for Enron when they were trying to break in to that state's electricity markets.

Charles Lewis of the Center for Public Integrity called Enron the number one career patron for George W. Bush, saying 'There was no company in America closer to George W. Bush than Enron.' You can draw your own conclusions from that statement just as you can draw your own conclusions from the next team report on corporate connections to the US Government coming up in a minute. But the short answer to your question is no, the Bushs' escaped any publically known consequences for their close relationship with Kenneth Lay who had donated enormous sums of money to their campaigns. Now let's hear from the team assigned to report on the United Fruit Company."

Student: "The United Fruit Company primarily traded in bananas farmed in third world countries and marketed in the United States and Europe. Its strategy was to build a monopoly by controlling the growing of bananas throughout central and South America by corrupting the governments of the poor underdeveloped countries much like the British East India Company did in India. At first they controlled the land and many of the essential services through ownership then sold off many of these holdings while creating and maintaining their monopoly through rights rather than direct ownership thus diverting many of the criticisms. Like the British East India Company they knew that rights trumped ownership. Essentially by controlling the economy of these countries they controlled the politics of the countries, eventually leading to the term 'banana republics.'"

Student: "Ultimately United Fruit merged with AMK, a company controlled by corporate raider Eli Black, and became known as United Brands which later became known as Chiquita Brands International. The company was associated with bribing government officials in exchange for lucrative monopolistic contracts that paid little taxes and exploiting its workers."

Student: "The only goal of the company was profits and they poured little back into the countries. There were oppositional rebellions and strikes and many people were killed. They had links to US government officials such as Secretary of State John Foster Dulles whose law firm represented United Fruit and whose brother Allen Dulles was the director of the CIA. In addition, a board member of United Fruit was the brother of Assistant Secretary of State for Inter-American Affairs John Moors Cabot who had been president of United Fruit and Ed Whitman who was United Fruit's principal lobbyist and married to President Eisenhower's personal secretary Ann C. Whitman. Eventually the U.S. Securities and Exchange Commission exposed the conspiracy to bribe the Honduran President with one and a quarter million dollars now and the promise of another one and a quarter million dollars later upon reduction of export taxes. In 1984, a CIA backed coup deposed the elected Guatemalan government of President Jacobo Árbenz in a move that favored the interest of the company and the private interests of Dulles brothers and others."

Student: "As we heard in a previous class, Eli Black the Company's CEO smashed the window of his 44th floor office with his attaché case and jumped to his death. He was 53 years old. Whether it was due to the stress of a financial set back or pending legal issues is unknown, but it was reported that his apparent focus on money had become his world."

Professor Meyer: "Thank you for that report. Are there any questions and comments?"

Student: "Professor, it would seem to me from these reports that all government is corrupt. Do you think that is true?"

Professor Meyer: "To the extent that governments are people, I think it is very likely that some corrupt people can be found in all governments. The quote attributed to Thomas Jefferson and others speaks to this, '*Eternal vigilance is the price of liberty*'; *power is ever stealing from the many to benefit the few.*'

Now let's hear from the team who reviewed the documentary entitled "The Corporation."

Student: "The documentary begins with an unusual detail that came from the 14th Amendment: Under constitutional law, corporations are seen as individuals. So documentary filmmaker Mark Achbar asks, what type of person would a corporation be? The evidence, according to such political activists as Noam Chomsky, filmmaker Michael Moore and company heads like carpet magnate Ray Anderson, points to a bad one. The documentary then goes on to expose IBM's Nazi ties and other large businesses' exploitation of human rights.

It further explains that a corporation is an artificial being, created by operation of law, with the right of succession and has the powers, attributes, and properties as expressly authorized by law or incident to its existence. What this means is the law seems to give corporations the same rights as a human being, only it never dies and has greater protections, which makes it a super human that can pry upon humans.

One of the central themes in the documentary is that corporations can be seen as monsters bent on taking control of public power and only focused on making money, regardless of the consequences.

The documentary asks Robert Hare, a consultant who helps the FBI profile its suspects, his diagnosis of corporations which is as follows: 'Corporations by definition have a personality disorder and can be categorized as psychopathic. Corporate psychopathic behavior describes a form of corporate conduct which meets the psychiatric criteria for human psychopathy, that is, a failure to conform to social norms and the violation of accepted ethical standards without remorse.

After all, a corporation's main job is to increase profit and make stockholders happy. Therefore, corporations will do anything to increase revenue, even if it means punishing the corporation's own workers. Workers of a corporation are often viewed as liabilities, not assets.'"

Professor Meyer: "What are some of the unethical immoral actions cited in the documentary?"

Student: "In the documentary they interview a man who was hired by a corporations to visit authoritarian governments in third world nations and offer them a deal they couldn't refuse just like in the movie *The Godfather*. The deal he offers them is the choice to become wealthy or in the alternative, they and their family may suffer, meaning they might be tortured and/or murdered."

Student: "Another example of immoral, unethical behavior in the Documentary involved Bechtel, a Pasadena,

California based corporation that made an unethical, immoral deal with the Bolivian government. In exchange for money bribes Bechtel got the rights to privatize the commodity of water then charged the people of Bolivia many of whom where living on two dollars a day up to twenty five percent of their income for water including the rain water that fell from the sky."

Student: "Corporations love authoritarian governments because they control the law, the people, and the natural resources, everything a corporation needs to maximize profits. General Motors, Ford, Coca Cola, IBM supported Hitler and Mussolini of the Nazi regime during WWII to maximize profits."

Professor Meyer: "Let's hold it there for a minute and discuss the U.S. Foreign Corrupt Practices Act (FCPA), a United States federal law that prohibits U.S. citizens and entities from bribing foreign government officials to benefit their business interests. Do you think this hurts U.S. companies who compete for business against foreign companies that are not prohibited from paying bribes?"

Student: "In my opinion it only challenges companies to work around it by spending millions of dollars indirectly to buy the same influence like paying bogus fines in foreign countries that find their way into the pockets of certain individuals."

Professor Meyer: "It's interesting that you should mention that. Years ago I was in the country of Panama talking to the captain of a U.S. Tuna boat who told me that they fish in Ecuadorian waters which according to a U.S. treaty with Ecuador were off limits and if they get caught they have to pay a fifty thousand dollar fine which in those days was the equivalent of three or four times that amount today. But the Captain told me the U.S. government reimbursed the company for the fine. He called it politics meaning a euphemism for unethical bribes to government officials in Ecuador.

And as a soldier in Vietnam I personally witnessed boat load after boat load of IBM punch cards being unloaded and I never saw or heard of an IBM punch card computer in the country. Also boat loads of broken office furniture. My immediate thought was somebody's making a lot of money off loading warehouses full of junk to the government. I had a strong sense that I was witnessing corporate/government corruption with little risk of accountability because in a war zone everything disappears without accountability. Please continue."

Student: "The documentary also explained how corporations condition the consumer by creating wants that can only be satisfied by consumption. How they mold people by seducing them through manufacturing desire that instills in them the belief that the good life can only obtained through consumption."

Student: "For me the most impactful moment in the documentary was listening to an investment banker recounting how in the very moment of 911 when the World Trade

Center buildings were falling down and people were jumping to their deaths, he was ecstatic because he knew his and his client's investments in gold would double in value due to the uncertainty the assault would cause in the stock market. He went on to say this was true of all the traders calling it "a blessing in disguise" and how it was the same during the bombing of Iraq when they couldn't wait until more bombs would rain down and destroy the oil wells so that their oil stocks would rise."

Professor Meyer: "That's a prime example of not seeing the forest of life for the trees of money. As psychologist Abraham Maslow wrote 'if all you have is a hammer everything looks like a nail.' Similarly Eknath Easwaran put it this way, if your focus is only on money and you see a thousands of years old giant redwood tree one of nature's most emotionally moving sights, all you see is the thirty or forty homes that can be built from that single tree. Such focus is a barrier between you and the true blessings of life that will enrich and sustain you through the vicissitudes that we all encounter on our journey. The myopic of self-gain will only bring you grief because enough will never be enough; you will be like Sisyphus in Greek mythology, condemned to rolling an immense boulder up a hill only for it to roll down every time it neared the top.

In a recent article I read about a small pharmacy in Florida that posted revenues of nearly 170 million dollars in one month not from filling prescriptions, but by filing lawsuits against drug makers that overcharged Medicare and Medicaid. In one California case the drug manufacturer sold a drug to providers for six dollars but billed Medi-Cal almost sixty dollars and in another they sold blood pressure medication to pharmacies for three dollars, but billed Medi-Cal seventy dollars for the same medications.

A recent *Wall Street Journal* article talked about the movie *Wall Street* and how the character Bud Fox wore a body wire and got his partner arrested for insider trading and how recently in real life a trader named David Slaine did the same thing after he told prosecutors that his good friend Craig Drimal traded on inside information. One of those arrested in the case was *Galleon* founder Raj Rajaratnan who pleaded not guilty and posted a one hundred million dollar bail. Another Anil Kumar pleaded guilty to insider trading and agreed to cooperate with the government, knowing as the old saying goes, 'the first to squeal gets the deal.'

Still another *Wall Street Journal* article compared Wall Street titans to stereotypical shady car salesmen because they got banks to make very risky loans then packaged those very risky loans with insurance and sold them off as securities knowing full well that many of the loans were going to fail. The packagers and sellers of the loans made their money in loan origination fees, insurance fees, packaging fees and selling fees under an 'I got mine that's all that matters' philosophy. In that article the former California state Treasurer compared their scheme to selling a car with faulty brakes and buying an insurance policy on the buyer of those cars; noting it was *Goldman's* practice to sell mortgage securities to investors, then bet that those securities would drop in value.

You would think with all this muck raking those responsible would be criminally punished and the company prohibited to do business forever rather than just admonished and fined a fraction of the ill-gotten gains, but in general that is not the case.

Here at GRU we once rented a University owned home to a Wall Street titan for seventy thousand dollars just for a week-end and after titan flew back on his private jet I read a news story that he had been accused of insider trading on a deal where he made a billion dollars, but was fined only two hundred million dollars which he gladly paid. From the perspective of financial gain, who wouldn't want to do that deal? I tell you these things because you will likely be tempted to do something similar more than once in your business career and you have to establish early on what kind of person and what kind of life you want to create for yourself, noting as we have here, there will always be consequences for your actions even if they are not immediately apparent. In his book *Small Is Beautiful* Schumacher argued that capitalism brought higher living standards at the cost of deteriorating culture.

Student: "Professor in this week's reading assignment from *Small Is Beautiful,* Schumacher writes in particular as it relates to many Corporations, 'An attitude to life which seeks fulfillment in the single-minded pursuit of wealth – in short, materialism – does not fit into this world, because it contains within itself no limiting principle, while the environment in which it is placed is strictly limited.'"

Professor Meyer: Thank you for that. It certainly is relevant to the conversations we are having on morals and ethics as an example of self-interest at the expense of everything else. Perhaps this is a good place for us to take a ten minute break and when you come back we'll hear from our guest speakers, three professionals not much older than you are, who have created successful, ethical careers in real estate."

Following the break.

Professor Meyer: "Two of the most common asset classes associated with wealth are paper equities and real estate. Our guest speakers today have built their wealth ethically through real estate each of them using a different approach. Here to talk to you about their careers and approaches, please welcome Adam Freeman, Rex Newmark and Joan Jacobs."

After a round of applause.

Adam Freeman: "Thank you. I appreciate the opportunity to be here. I began my real estate career brokering single family residential. I learned a lot and made some good money through commissions. But one of the things I learned was that my personality was more suited for commercial real estate where clients are typically making business decisions rather than in residential where decisions tend to be decidedly more personal and emotional. In addition, the dollar value of commercial transactions is usually more which means more commission. The field of

commercial real estate covers both the listing and sale of office and retail space along with leasing. As a residential real
estate broker when you lease a property the commission
may be six to ten percent of say a three thousand dollar a
month home or apartment which translates to six to ten
percent of thirty six thousand dollars for a one year lease.
That's three thousand six hundred dollars in commission
to be split four ways between the listing and selling brokers
and their respective offices. Compare this to leasing fifty
thousand square feet of office for a six percent commission
which at forty two dollars per square foot per year times say
a ten year lease that's one million two hundred and sixty
dollars in commissions also split four ways. And when you
sell an office building for fifty or sixty million dollars or
more at four to six percent commission you get paid well
for your efforts. In addition, your clients are corporate executives who are basing their decisions on data and have
the financial capability to follow through rather than just
hoping to get a loan. Not that you can't make a good living, even a very good living, selling residential real estate
especially with home prices in some areas as high as commercial properties, but what you choose to do has a lot to
do with your personality and personal preference. In single
family residential you often spend your day driving people
from house to house hoping to find the one they are going
to connect with, and hoping when you do, they will still
like it after they sign the purchase agreement and won't get
buyer's remorse then change their minds. And too, that
they will qualify for the loan. Homes do fall out of escrow
based on those things while it is rare for that to happen in

commercial real estate. In contrast to driving people from home to home I spend most of my days in meetings with executives and showing a select few buildings and spaces.

I also invest in commercial real estate by syndicating office and retail properties and have accumulated a portfolio of equity. Commercial tenants typically lease for long terms with options to renew at higher market rates. They pay down my debt and increase my income through the higher rents. Plus I get the benefits of writing off the expenses associated with managing the properties in addition to depreciation and tax deferred appreciation. Compared to residential property, commercial properties are much easier to manage and when I retire, the properties I own will be paid for free and clear and provide me with a good deal of passive income. I see a hand up."

Students: "Yes, I'm wondering if you need a different real estate license for commercial rather than residential."

Adam Freeman: "The license is the same for both. I should add for those who don't know, there are two types of real estate licenses, one is called a Salesperson and the other is a Broker. A salesperson license allows you to do everything a broker's license does but you have to work under the supervision of a Broker. Whereas with a Broker's license you can either affiliate with a brokerage company as a broker associate or go out on your own. Questions?"

Student: "Yes. How do you get into the business when there's so much competition?

Adam Freeman: "That's a good question. Without clients you will not make any money and there are a lot of brokers chasing clients. The simple answer is that you have to hustle; have a good work ethic, and work smarter and harder. Most business dealings boil down to relationships and good relationships are built on trust and that takes time and effort. It's a two-way street, the client has to trust you and you have to trust the client. If there is a breach of that trust there is no basis on which you can do business. If a client says I'll have my bank transfer the money tomorrow and it doesn't come you immediately have to question whether you can trust that client. And not only that, your reputation in the industry with other brokers and clients especially on the other side of the deal will also be compromised. Word gets out that you can't be trusted to perform and others will not want to do business with you. It's the same with your representations to your client. If you misrepresent something intentionally or even unintentionally or fail to perform they will likely not do business with you and tell their friends not to do business with you. You live and die on your reputation of being able to perform and your reputation for honesty and integrity."

Professor Meyer: "Thank you Adam, that's a good place to stop so we can hear from the others. After hearing from each of our guest speakers we'll open the floor for questions in a panel format. Next up Rex Newmark.

Rex Newmark: "Thank you. Like Adam, I worked for one of the foremost real estate brokerage companies specializing in commercial real estate and I concur with Adam that the most important tool you have in your tool box is your ethics. It's a very competitive business and there's a fair share of brokers and clients who will sell you and or their clients out to make a few dollars more. But while they may cheat you in a deal their reputation will ultimately relegate them to only doing business with those who will cheat them in a deal. It's the old story of there's no honor among thieves and they always have to watch their backs knowing that those they do business with are out to get them. Their survival depends on cheating and justifying it by saying, 'it's nothing personal, it's just business.' True they make a living, sometimes a very good living, but if that's the way you want to live your life always looking over your shoulder knowing you can't trust anybody, that's up to you. That said, there are a lot of good, honest, hardworking ethical brokers and clients too. Learning who you can trust and who you can't is part of the learning curve in becoming a successful broker.

Unlike Adam I no longer, with rare exception, broker transactions. But like Adam I invest in commercial real estate and have built up a portfolio of properties that has become my business and provides me with a good income. My personal style of investing is a bit different than his and contrary to one of the primary attractions of real estate investing, that of leverage. For those who do not know about leverage, I'll explain.

One of the key advantage to investing in real estate is leverage. Leverage means you only need to put down fifteen or twenty percent of the total purchase price to acquire a property and you get one hundred percent ownership control of that property including any appreciation in value. For example you can acquire a million dollar property using only two hundred thousand dollars of your capital. Let's say in two or three years after you purchase the property its market value appreciates ten percent. It's now worth one million one hundred thousand dollars, that means you have made one hundred thousand dollars on your two hundred thousand dollars; that's a fifty percent return in only a few years. That's pre-tax, but the tax is not payable unless you sell the property so even the taxable gain is working for you. You can even delay paying that tax almost indefinitely through something call a tax deferred exchange where instead of selling the building you trade it for another building of equal or greater value. In addition to these benefits you are entitled to certain write-offs and off-sets generated by the cost of owning and managing the property. These include items like depreciation and maintenance. Simply put, depreciation is an income tax deduction that allows a taxpayer to recover the cost for the property's reduction in value due to physical deterioration, functional obsolescence and economic obsolescence. It's often referred to as a "phantom" expense because the IRS does not actually write you a check, they are merely allowing you to take a tax deduction based on the perceived decrease in the value.

Depreciation assumes that the investment property is actually declining in value over time as a result of those factors, but we know this is often not the case. In good areas the value of property is often appreciating. As a result of real estate depreciation however, the investor may actually have cash flow from the property, yet show a tax loss. This is one of the many advantages why people invest in real estate.

After telling you the advantages of leverage you many wonder why I give it up in favor of my investment strategy which is to buy stand alone, single tenant, triple net, commercial properties for all cash. First I'll explain what those terms mean. A single tenant standalone building is one that has no other buildings attached to it, one building on one parcel of land with only one tenant like a Burger King or a Jiffy Lube or a Dollar General store. Triple net means in addition to the rent, the tenant has to pay all the property taxes, all the insurance costs and all the maintenance costs, so the income I receive is all mine subject only to state and federal taxes. I still get the benefits of appreciation and depreciation along with rental increases per the terms of the lease and deductions for management costs like travel to inspect the property which is especially nice for my properties in vacation areas like Florida in the winter and California in the summer.

The advantage of this strategy for me is more certainty of income and less management demands on my time; managing real estate can be very time consuming. I mitigate risk by only purchasing property with highly rated tenants. On the down side, should a property become vacant my income stops and my expenses accelerate. That's why choosing a property with a highly rated tenant is very important. Over the years my return on investment has exceeded twenty percent with less volatility and more control than my investments in the stock market. There's not a lot a minor shareholder can do to effect good management of a company, but with a vacant building I can be very creative in getting it released."

Professor Meyer: "Thanks Rex this will be a good place to stop so we can hear from our third presenter GRU alumna Joan Jacobs about her real estate strategy after which we will open the floor for Q & A. Joan."

Joan Jacobs: "Thank you Professor. When I was an undergrad at GRU I met Professor Meyer and he gave me some real estate investing advice saying I should plan a strategy to acquire a few good rental properties with the idea that in ten or fifteen years I would likely have enough equity and income that I could chose to work part time or even stop work; meaning I could semi-retire or retire in my mid to late thirties if I wished. That sounded pretty good to me.

Following graduation I went to work for a media company representing them in the western market place. It was an entry level position, but I was single and it paid a pretty good salary so I made a commitment to save fifty percent of my net income toward purchasing my first property. Professor Meyer told me that the best tenant I could have is myself and that buying an owner occupied home is usually easier and less challenging than buying a non-owner occupied investment property in terms of getting a loan. But by the end of my first year I did not have enough money for a conventional down payment so I took his advice and started looking for a home that was 'for sale by owner'. Owners who are offering their home for sale directly to the public rather than going through a real estate broker usually do so to avoid paying a five, six or seven percent commission which could add up to a lot of money. The advantage to a buyer like me is that a 'for sale by owner' seller might be open to creative terms like a rent to buy arrangement which means you rent the property until such a time you can afford to buy it; sometimes this also means a portion of the rent you pay will go toward the down payment. Or the seller might possibly carrying back the loan for a period of time which would provide the seller with a good income stream and better tax advantages by spreading out their taxable gain over a period of years rather than in one lump sum, which would be the case in an outright purchase; the seller not only saves money on commissions, but on taxes too. Another advantage to a buyer like me could be a lower down payment and an automatic source for a loan without having to meet stricter loan approval criterion and the typical loan fees banks and mortgage companies charge. This also includes the opportunity to negotiate terms such as interest rate and monthly payment amounts that are more in line with what I can afford.

Long story short I found a home where the elderly seller was looking to sell to a nice young person like me just starting off in life like she once did. Besides not having to pay a commission, by carrying back the loan it provided her with a monthly income to live on. I only had to put five percent down and she carried the loan for five years giving me time to find a conventional lender to pay her the balance. Since she was moving to an assisted living apartment she also included a lot of the furnishings. I now had a place to live and my first real estate investment with a reliable tenant.

Three years later my income was much higher and I qualified for a conventional loan. By then the property appraised for a lot more. I paid off the seller and was able to take out enough cash to not only get my initial five percent back, but put a down payment on a second home which I moved into to qualify for a more favorable owner occupied loan, then rented out my first home. By then I had also obtained a real estate license and used the commission I received in representing myself on the second home as part of the down payment. The following year my new home appraised for enough that I was able to take out a second loan on it and used that money to buy a for sale by owner duplex. I then moved into one side of the duplex and rented out my second home plus the other side of the duplex. I now had some passive income along with write offs on my taxes from owning what amounted to three income properties; two single family homes and half of a duplex. The units on the duplex were both large and located in a nice area so I decided to convert each of them into a condo so I could sell each side to separate buyers for a lot more money than selling the building as a duplex. With the proceeds from the sale of the one unit I was able to buy a fourth home to use as a rental. So ten years after my graduation from GRU I had enough income that I could quit work if I wanted to and live off the income stream. That was not my plan, but I did take a year off to travel around Europe. I now have the option to find a job that I like and work part time or not work at all."

Professor Meyer: "Thank you Joan. Now's a good time to take questions for any of the presenters."

Student: "First, thank all of you for your presentations. I found them very interesting. You've inspired me to follow in your footsteps. I have a question for Adam. How much money can you make a year leasing and selling commercial real estate? And how long does it typically take to get started before you can make a good living?"

Adam Freeman: "That depends on you; how smart and how hard you are willing to work. Even if you are affiliated with a major company you are still working for yourself. You are your own boss and your own employee. To those who are use to a nine to five job this may sound great, sleep in now and then, go to the beach when you want, take a trip without having to think about when to get back, but not everyone is disciplined enough to be their own boss. You can make hundreds of thousands of dollars a year in this business, but it is also a very, very competitive field and you can work eighteen hour days for months without earning a cent all while having to pay for your clothes, cars, gas, rent, food etc. When I first started it took me six months before I saw a dime. You can also give everything you've got in the way of time, expertise and energy to a client and a deal, only to have it all fall through and end up with nothing. This is especially hard when you were counting on the money to pay your bills. If you can't handle this level of uncertainty and the emotional ups and downs it's not a business for you. If you can, the rewards can be great. "

Student: "I have a question for Joan. How hard is it to find a 'for sale by owner' and make deals like you described?"

Joan Jacobs: "They are not easy to find. It's a competitive market place; nothing is easy, you have to work at it and have some luck too. But here's the thing, I believe the cornerstone of most if not all business is people and if you hit it off with a person anything and I mean anything is possible. I know people who have sold their property to others knowingly below market solely because they liked the buyer. You might have heard that the best business deals are made on the golf course and that's because it's where people get to know each other and people like to do business with those they know. That's universal."

Student: "This question's for Joan. What are some of the risks associated with buying and renting homes like you did? You make it sound much too easy."

Joan Jacobs: "One of the risks of course is that you can't make the payments on your obligations. Perhaps you lost your job or one or more of your tenants can't pay you so you can't pay your bills; it's a domino effect. Vacancy is always a weak link. A tenant moves out and it can take months before you can find another tenant and during that time you have to make up for that loss of income. Or worse they don't pay the rent and won't move out which forces you into a costly legal process called eviction. Or the property you bought needs a new roof, a new sewer line or other expensive repair. Failure to make needed repairs might target you as a bad landlord and the courts can get involved. And failure to pay your bills will affect your credit rating which will make it near impossible to get loans. I might add too when it comes to purchasing 'for sale by owner' properties you best get some outside advice before you sign a contract with the Seller so you are aware of all the pitfalls such as if you miss one payment you lose certain rights. In the past some such contracts did not transfer equity until the last payment was made which meant you could have made every payment for twenty years, but missed the last one and have nothing to show for it. Thankfully the law has since protected against this, but there are other terms you should check very carefully. You should also get a professional property inspection and title insurance before closing the deal."

Student: "This is for Joan too. What do you do when you can't pay because of the reasons you mentioned?"

Joan Jacobs: "First off you have to plan for those contingencies not wait for them to happen then try to figure out what to do. If you have private seller carry back financing you might be able to renegotiate to make partial payments until your situation is resolved or even a moratorium on payments. In some cases you might even be able to do this with a conventional lender like a bank; remember the bank is really the person sitting in front of you and if he or she likes you they will want to help. My advice is always be honest with your creditors so that they feel they can trust you and never betray that trust; once lost it may take a long time to regain it, if ever. This is where a lot of people fail. They consider themselves honest and ethical until their back is up against the wall then they resort to being dishonest and unethical out of fear for the consequences. It is better to lose the asset than lose the trust. It's easier to get another deal when you are honest and ethical because people will sense it and want to do business with you. If you can't meet your obligations be proactive, contact your creditor first, be honest and work something out that you both can live with. This requires you to understand their side too. Always remember whatever the situation, it too will pass, but don't stand around and do nothing while waiting."

Student: "This is for Joan. How can you get a tenant to move out and avoid the expense of having to go to court and evict them?"

Joan Jacobs: "Your only protection is a tenant who values their credit rating because the eviction process will hurt their credit rating and they will be a lot more willing to work with you to avoid that. You may feel you are pretty smart, but it's very easy to be conned by dishonest or desperate people. Less so as you gain experience, but nobody no matter how savvy they might be, is immune to a good con. To be frank, many landlords when they find themselves in a situation with a difficult tenant offer the tenant money to move. It hurts, but it is often a lot less expensive than going to court and then when you get possession of your property, find it trashed with little or no recourse against your deadbeat tenant.

Student: "That's terrible having to pay a tenant who owes you money."

Joan Jacobs: "It can be emotionally challenging unless you look at it as strictly a business decision."

Student: "I have a question for Rex. How long did it take you to get enough money to pay all cash for a property?"

Rex Newmark: "I started by investing in leveraged real estate deals and in the stock market. Then took my profits and starting buying for all cash because as I said, I have better control over the dips in the economy and I did not want to be burdened with management. With this strategy I can do the things that are more important to me like traveling. Everything in life is a tradeoff."

Student: "This question is for Adam. You mentioned at one point you started syndicating property, can you explain how that is done?"

Adam Freeman: "Through syndication you can purchase a property you are not financially able to purchase by yourself. With a syndicate, investors pool their resources and share in both the risks and the rewards of owning real estate. A syndicate is basically a form of partnership with the syndicator as the lead partner who finds the property and manages the partnership on behalf of the partners. The investors are typically locked in for an agreed term or until the syndicator decides on when to sell or refinance the property.

Student: "How much can you make as a syndicator?"

Adam Freeman: "The syndicator typically gets between 25% and 50% of the distributable cash generated from operations, refinance or sale of a property."

Student: "This question is for Rex. How do you find good deals on single tenant, triple net commercial properties? And how come if the tenants are so financially strong they just don't buy the property themselves rather than pay rent?"

Rex Newmark: "Those are two very good questions. I subscribe to publications that list commercial properties for sale all across the country and additionally do research on the Internet. Many companies especially franchisors don't want to use their cash to buy expensive real estate and especially small parcels here and there in towns and cities across the country. They're not in the real estate business, but the specialty of their franchise be it a Jiffy Lube or a Burger King or a Dollar General store. Why would they want their money tied up in a lot in some out-of-the-way town should their franchisee fail? There are some exceptions like McDonald's where the Franchisor does own the land under many of their franchisees."

Professor Meyer: "We only have time for one more question."

Student: "How can we get in touch with each of you if we have any more questions and would that be okay?"

Professor Meyer: "Each of our guest speakers have graciously agreed to let me publish their email address on the Course Website. Let's have a round of applause to show our appreciation to Adam, Rex and Joan."

Following the applause the speakers leave.

"Professor Meyer: "Don't forget your Assignment for Class Seven to write a Final Reflection Paper of approximately ten to fifteen pages, double spaced, although length is not as important as depth, chronicling your personal journey of discovery in this Course. Feel free to express yourself in any style or form you want. Cite personal examples and situations in your life or this Course that have helped you develop the analytical thinking necessary to come to terms with your discovery. How has the Course challenged, influenced or changed your beliefs or behavior? What has been the most difficult issue or issues for you to explore? What topic, issue or person most influenced your thinking and why or how? From your prospective what place does conscious have in commerce. The Paper should be road map of your journey through the Course and what you have gained or not, from it. One more thing, next week we are going to have a guest speaker from the financial management industry and instead of speaking toward the end of the class he will do so at the beginning so make sure you come on time. I look forward to seeing you then and hearing about your individual journey. Have a good rest of the week. We stand adjourned.

CLASS SEVEN

FINAL REFLECTION PAPERS

Professor Meyer: "Welcome back. This is the day when we get to hear from each of you as you reflect on what you have gained from the Course and share those insights with your fellow classmates. But before we do, we have a brief, but insightful presentation from our final guest speaker of the Course on the topic of financial management.

By way of introduction, Jess Talbott is a graduate of GRU who has distinguished himself as one of the stars in the financial management industry as noted in the annual Forbes Magazine's listing of top financial managers in the Country. I will note too, according to serval Internet references, financial management is one of the highest income earning careers. What makes Jess a standout however, is not just his financial success, but his strict code of fidelity to morals and ethics. I think when you hear his presentation and interact with him during the Q&A session you will see this for yourselves. Please give Jess a warm welcome.

Following applause.

Jess Talbott: "Thank you, it feels good to be back home at GRU. Following graduation I got my securities license and joined the Wall Street firm of Goldman Sachs where I met my wife Gina who was also GRU graduate. Two years after meeting we got married and decided to leave Goldman and move back here because we did not like the morals and ethics of Wall Street where money seemed to matter more than the clients themselves. Shortly after we arrived I started to work for a financial management group that already had a portfolio in the hundreds of millions of dollars. However, it wasn't the size of the portfolio that attracted me, but that the bulk of their clients were middle class working people like my and Gina's parents, and that the managers genuinely cared for them. I knew immediately it was the corporate culture I was looking for.

When I joined the firm I was fortunate to be mentored by the group's founder and years later after I had developed a sizable portfolio of my own, he retired and selected me to take over the leadership role. By then our portfolio was more than twice as large as it had been when I started.

As an investment advisor based in the West, you have to be at the office well before the market opens so if you are not a morning person this is not the industry for you, especially in the winter months when it's dark outside and you have to get up while others are still asleep. Besides starting each day well before dawn it is a very stressful business. Stressful because of the level of responsibility your clients have entrusted to you. It requires a strong desire to be of service to others with an inner drive to succeed for them first and yourself second.

Starting off, it often takes years of marketing yourself to those you meet at community centric events like charities, churches and service clubs, to build a relationship of trust. But it is also a very rewarding knowing how important you are to your clients.

When Gina and I married we pledged to lead a balanced life. We now have three children who are involved in school, sports, music, homework, chores, church and charity work. Both Gina and I want our children to experience the joy of childhood yet learn to be responsible adults with a good work ethic that includes giving back to others. Our parenting philosophy is not to educate our children to be rich, but to be happy so when they grow up they will know the value of things, not just the price of them.

Like you I was a student in Professor Meyer's class and during that time he talked about the part real estate plays in building wealth and balancing your investments; in fact he helped Gina and I get our first home. Since then we have purchased nine other single family homes in good neighborhoods as rentals. Gina manages them while I concentrate on our paper investments along with those of my clients. Given that my time here today is limited, instead of speaking in general, perhaps it's best for me to ask if you have any questions."

Student: "What licenses do you need to do the work you do and are they difficult to get?"

Jess Talbott: "The basic license is a Series 7. Fortunately there are many schools that teach you how to pass the test. If you want to know where to find one you can do an Internet search or feel free to contact me."

Student: "Thank you."

Student: "Jess, you lucked out meeting someone who took you under his wing, but what if you don't know anybody, how do you get started?"

Jess Talbott: "Good firms are always looking for good people because you only get paid when you bring in business. To get started you need to research different firms then go on interviews prepared with questions that will help you decide if the firm's culture is in line with your personal philosophy. It's similar to serious dating, you are looking for the right long term partner.

Student: "Thank you."

Jess Talbott: "Before we run out of time, I want to be sure to share with you more of my philosophy for success in any business. There will likely come a point in your careers where you can make more money by telling half-truths or even three quarter truths to others by editorializing information so that it favors you more than your clients. It may not be illegal, but it might as well be, because once you cross that line your relationship with yourself and others will never be the same and you will regret it for the rest of your life. You can always make money, but it is very difficult to regain trust and self-esteem. A moment ago I mentioned choosing a good company is like choosing a lifelong partner. A good partnership can only flourish when each partner puts the other's interest ahead of their own and it's the same in business where your clients are your partners. 'When in doubt spell it out' is a good fundamental for any relationship. Be honest and tell the client everything he or she needs to know when helping them make a decision. Treat them as you would want to be treated if your roles were reversed. Be fearless in your faith that fair dealing will always trump personal gain in making a decision. And that the best outcome will always be the best outcome for your clients even if it means a short term loss to you personally. In the long term you will prosper when you put your clients first."

Student: "How do you know what's best for your client?"

Jess Talbott: "Ask them what their objectives are and share with them what you know. Give scenarios such as this might happen if you do this, and that might happen if you do that. Help them to evaluate their own tolerance for risk. Don't sugar coat and err on the side of conservatism. Challenge them to make sure they understand the risks and can live with the consequences. When you do this it lifts a huge burden from your shoulders."

Professor Meyer: "Thank you Jess for that valuable advice. I know you have to get back to the office and appreciate that you took these few minutes to stop by. I'm certain your advice has simplified the decision making process for everyone by making it easier for them to know what to do. All decisions come with consequences and they have to ask themselves if they are prepared to live with those consequences. Let's thank Jess for his insights into what it's like to be a financial manager and his sage advice on leading a moral and ethical life."

Following applause Jess Talbott leaves.

Professor Meyer: Next up are the presentations of your Final Reflection Papers. Feel free to speak extemporaneously or read from your Papers, your choice. When one person is finished just raise your hand to be next so we can hear from as many of you as we can before having to vacate the room for the next class. Who wants to start off?"

Student: "The best way I can describe this class is, it is like that old adage 'give a man a fish, you feed him for a day, teach him how to fish and you feed him for a lifetime.' I was hoping to receive definitive yes and no answers for all the questions I presented in my pre-course paper, but what I got was even more valuable, a way to find the answers for myself."

Student: "To paraphrase Malcolm Forbes, the purpose of education is to replace an empty mind with an open one. That statement sums up what I believe to have been the primary objective of this class. Although there were other objectives such as to learn the methods by which we can build wealth, morally and ethically the most important lessons were about critical thinking as necessary to maintain an open mind.

What came out of our class discussion is that we should avoid blanket acceptance of collective ideas and examine them critically before making decisions. I believe most of us were not used to approaching society in this manner.

Another major benefit of this Class that I personally found was in our evaluation of how to become wealthy in an intelligent manner. It really gave me a perspective on the issue that I had never seen because of my interactions with wealthy people who love to spend money on a daily basis. This class provided me the benefit to re-evaluate my position on wealthy living.

To quote one of Professor Meyer's favorite philosophers Bertrand Russel, 'if thought is to become the possession of man, not the privilege of the few, we must be done with fear. It is fear that holds us back – fear least their cherished beliefs should prove delusions; fear least the institutions by which they lie should prove harmful; fear least themselves should prove less worthy of respect than they have supposed themselves to be.'

I have witnessed the effects that a person's social circle can have on a person's thought process, and I worry that the progress made in this Class might be lost for some of the students when they return back to their environment especially when it comes to the issue of religion. Religion is one of my favorite issues to discuss not because I am a religious person, but quite the opposite, I am perplexed by the extent to which people are accepting to indisputably abide by their religion's laws. How they can so easily accept everything their religion says and does. It is even harder when I know that if another entity had been responsible for half the harm that most religions have done, not only would the people not accept it, they would insist on abolishing it from society. The greatest irony is that religious people tend to be so critical of other ideas. Faith means making a virtue out of not thinking. And those who preach faith and enable and elevate it are intellectual slave holders, keeping mankind in a bondage to fantasy and nonsense that has spawned and justified so much lunacy and destruction. To quote Rev. Peter Gomes minister of Harvard University's Memorial Church, we do not preach what Jesus preached, Instead we preach Jesus." And in his book *The Scandalous Gospel of Jesus*, he quotes Bishop Desmond Tutu and the African proverb, 'when the white Christians came to Africa they had the Bible and the Africans had the land. Then the Africans were given the Bible and the white Christians took the land.' 'The only appropriate attitude for man to have about the big question is not the arrogant certitude that is the hallmark of religion, but doubt. Doubt is humble and that is what man needs to be considering that human history is just a litany of getting shit dead wrong." Bill Maher, Religious.

Another aspect of the class that ranked very high in my experience and my willingness to participate in debate was the discussion of controversial issues. It is always interesting to see how the reality that each of us grew up with can affect how differently we see things. More often than not, the most controversial cases are the ones that provide the easiest proof of the benefits of critical thinking and give the greatest clarity on the notion of right and wrong. For example the discussion on child labor raised a number of interesting issues that would need to be examined before banning the notion. One issue is should age matter if that person needs to work in order to survive and to help their family survive. I was pleasantly surprised to see that the attitude of the class shifted from being strongly against the notion of child labor to evoking skepticism and uncertainty. Some of the other issues raised that provided interesting debate were the reliability of history and statistics and the general notion of what is considered right and wrong. These are all ideas and practices that humans dictate and only when it becomes clear to people can critical thinking be achieved.

Albert Einstein said "It is the supreme art of the teacher to awaken joy in creative expression and knowledge. The absolute, most important and compelling dynamic of the class's effectiveness was the ability of the professor to be a reliable authority and mentor. When a professor presents himself as a unique example of open-mindedness and literally practices what he preaches, then the task of influencing his students becomes easier to accomplish because the students are already brought into the idea. Hopefully I will be able to partake in a similar excursion and have the opportunity to really get in touch with myself and explore who I am without the noise of society.

'I cannot afford to waste my time making money (Jean Louis Rodolph Agassiz) the reality is that money becomes a hurdle instead of a tool at times.' The most important lesson I learned from this class was that I do not need money to attain my goals. That trying to make money as so perfectly expressed by Agassiz can come in the way of finding the time to accomplish our true goals in life.

I would like to note that this class was the most rewarding and satisfying class I have ever had. Not only because it taught me some new things about myself and about life, but also because I witnessed the evolvement towards a more enlightened mind for the rest of the students. I have been exposed to the thought process of individuals who think differently than me about certain issues, something that I had usually not given much attention to in the past. While I don't believe we are all leaving this class in an identical state of open mindedness or that was the original expectation, I believe we are all leaving this class with a more open mind than we started with. We experienced a learning process in which we all taught one another something. The end result has been that the brain has been stimulated to the idea and importance of critical thinking. I believe this quote from Daniel J. Kurland summarizes quite explicitly the characteristic of true critical thinking, 'Thus, critical thinking involves following evidence where it leads; considering all possibilities; relying on reason rather than emotion; being precise; considering a variety of possible viewpoints and explanations; weighing the effects of motives and biases; being concerned more with finding the truth than with being right; not rejecting unpopular views out of hand; being aware of one's own prejudices and biases; and not allowing them to sway one's judgment.'"

Professor Meyer: Thank you for that passionate report. Who's next?"

Student: "When I started business school, one of the driving forces for my decision was to find a good job where I had the opportunity to become successful which to me meant becoming rich and powerful. I had dreams of making a huge amount of money, buying expensive cars, mansions in up-scale neighborhoods, a powerful and successful job and spending fortunes on expensive items. This dream is the lifestyle that celebrities' live and that we regularly watch on television. For my generation they represent the role model of the 21st century and is automatically associated with happiness. Yet more and more I hear or read that these same wealthy people regularly see therapists or get hooked into abusing alcohol and drugs, hurting those around them, even killing themselves. Their ethics and morals seem to have faded too. They have become unable to cope with their admired life. I started to think about the question what makes us happy and what role does work, power, success and wealth have in our perceptions; and how to live a fulfilling life with a successful career that I can agree with both ethically and morally.

Researching the origin of the word 'wealthy' opened up a new perspective for me. 'Wealthy' derives from the Old English world 'weal' (well-being) (and the condition) which together means 'the condition of well-being'

(Anielski, 2003). It is about being able to balance and enjoy what is important to me in life.

Our discussion in class about Gandhi's so called seven social sins (Easwaran, 2000) provided a tangible guide to better understanding how to achieve real wealth. His *'Wealth without Work'* where people, especially the younger generation have become wealthy without any effort or work and thus are unable to value their prosperous life and lack ideals and goals. His *'Pleasure without Conscience'* points to the state where our happiness depends only on our own possessions and satisfactions and consequently neglecting compassion for others. His *Knowledge without Character* means having knowledge without a strong, well-grounded character and is as dangerous as having no knowledge. His *'Commerce without Morality'* talks about the fact we have created an economy that is based on profit operating without a moral foundation. *'Science without Humanity'* warns us of becoming slaves to our own technology by depriving the science of a higher human aspect. *'Religion without Sacrifice'* refers to the façade we present when preaching religion on one side, but on the other side being resistant to others real life suffering. *'Politics without principle'* describes today's political superficial image of working for the greater good for society, yet pursuing his or her own selfish goals. I started asking myself what is important to me, what role does money, success and power play in my life and how I can make a contribution to a better society."

Professor Meyer: "Thank you for that inspiration. Who is next?"

Student: "For many people just like me, success is when they get admiration from other people and feel superior. By getting attention we feel special and stand out amongst them. While success used to be based on the output or product before the industrial revolution in the 19th century, life's focus and definition of success has changed. We were able to refine production, decrease production time by introducing division of labor. Now everything has to go fast. Everything is focused on profit. No wasting time or making mistakes because this would have a negative effect on revenue and profit (Schumacher, 1989). But while it increased our standard of living, it also had a major effect on our personal and social life and the importance of being successful and powerful. Generally we have become so far apart from the work itself (Huxley's essay on the Industrial revolution). By introducing division of labor, people decreased production time on the one hand, but on the other hand also deprived workers from achieving success by seeing the outcome of their work.

As a business student this course made me think critically about the overall importance of morals and ethics. Especially when looking at powerful managers during the financial crisis who had knowledge, but lacked ethics, and lost enormous amounts of investor's money while still being rewarded with huge bonuses. Many people lost their savings, had to move out of their homes and ultimately were unable to pay bills because those managers misused their power for their own selfish greed. Ethics are defined as the values a person develops over time and represent how one lives his or her life. They help us to shape our personality, our value system and are the foundation of who we are as a person. Yet, not living by these values over a longer period of time can has severe consequences. I remember the Professor saying in class that he appreciated being able to sleep well each night. Seeing these business persons destroying innocent people's lives by making decisions that only benefited themselves, made me wonder whether they followed values at all or what kind of values they had. It was interesting too when the Professor raised the question in class if anyone would work for a tobacco company, many in the class felt uncertain even though the effects of tobacco consumption are well known, ethical issues still arose for everyone in the class."

Professor Meyer: "Thank you for sharing that reflection. Who's next?"

Student: "I have always looked at money as something that rewards my hard work. Instead this class has given me a different perspective. Rather than just seeing it as a reward, you can have it work for you. One of the most impressive examples that had a major impact on me was reading in *The Millionaire Next Door* and *Your Money or Your Life*, the example of Nate. I never considered that you could accumulate about $304,000 within 20 years by saving $5 per week. This means by having one drink or one lunch less per week one could accumulate the same amount, which is easily manageable. It is often the small things that we do not think about that actually make up a big sum in the end. This made me track my expenditures.

I started dividing them up in an equal manner, such as groceries, eating out, books for school, clothes etc. My intention was to figure out how much money I really spent on these supposedly small things. Although most things only cost a few dollars and I didn't even realize I bought them, it became a huge amount at the end of the month. Especially during the little exercise to track our expenses that Professor Meyer assigned us to do; I was shocked. I was absolutely not aware of the amount of money I actually spent. I bought each item instantly when it came to mind.

The journal exercise assignment about living 'one day without spending a cent' also opened my eyes. First, I was still able to do it easily and second I felt better at the end of the day because I was proud of myself for not spending anything. Since then I am more aware of what I am spending and I ask myself twice before buying it and what I need it for. I tried to cut down on the little things such as a Starbuck's coffee. The story our guest speaker told reminded me of Professor Meyer' words, 'Small items tend to only give you pleasure for the moment, but as soon as you have it another desire comes up. I never noticed this before until Professor Meyer pointed out the differences between desire, pleasure and joy. While desire and pleasure are short term, joy is a lasting state of being. I realized that I did not know what enough meant to me, my intention was to have short sighted pleasure. Now I ask myself whether I am just following my desire by buying an item and in doing so have been able to decrease my spending and in the process learn what enough means to me."

Professor Meyer: Thank you for that. Well said. Next?"

Student: "This Class truly furthered my interest in becoming financially wealthy and gave me an abundance of information and help to move forward with. First I found the living within your means or frugality portion of acquiring wealth very interesting. It was intriguing to me that this did not have to mean living a Spartan life, rather it is different for every individual depending on what their means are, such as the case of being able to purchase a Rolls Royce while still living below your means.

I found the idea of keeping a separate linked account a great idea as a way of saving apart from day to day banking. Also it was very helpful to learn about investing in the real estate market and ways to build income through acquiring property. I had never given much thought to owning property prior to taking this class and now I find myself researching properties in the areas where I may be placed for work next year. Not only that, but I am looking for live/ work space so that my mortgage can be paid off from the commercial tenants on the property. These types of ideas had never even crossed my mind before taking this Class, but now I find myself trying to think outside the box and think of new ways to acquire wealth and live more frugally at the same time.

In the acquiring power portion of this Class I learned how to overcome desires and contribute to the wealth of nature and the world which is a very difficult thing to do and can seem overwhelming at times. Due to the many discussions, tips and journal exercises such as mantra, meditation, preferences vs addiction I feel very confident about my future ability to overcome those desires that might pull me in a direction I don't really want to go. This is truly an amazing feeling to know that I have the power to control or even change my desires for the betterment of myself and those around me and society. Gaining this kind of power was something that I had never imagined I would learn or would even be covered when I first started this course. I wish that I would have learned how to work on myself in these ways when I was younger, it would have led to quite a few more smarter decisions on my part and a more fulfilling life.

The second part of acquiring power for me was learning how powerful one person can be in helping nature and the world. Easwaran's '*The Compassionate Universe*' struck a chord with me and it is a book that I will pass on to anyone that will sit down and absorb the material. I find it funny to think back before the first Class reviewing the books that I had to read for this class and I remember thinking that '*The Compassionate Universe*' was probably the one book that I was going to struggle through. I could not have been any more wrong, by the time I finished the second chapter of the book I could not put it down and I could not stop discussing the book with my girlfriend and anybody else who would listen. I had finally found a book, an author that made me feel that I had a chance to make a difference in the environment. Each story Easwaran told only strengthened my resolve that I had the power to make a difference and that I could influence others to do the same. I now find myself doing all the small things that may not seem like much, but I know will have an impact in the long run. It is a thrilling emotion to feel as though I am in a position of power and not of power over others rather of power over myself.

The definition of success that I came into this class with and the one that I will leave with are very different. This difference has mostly to do with the strengthening of my resolve to take control of my life and make decisions that will give me true happiness. Having the confidence and freedom to make choices and live the life that I want to live. Prior to this class I often thought of success as solely related to the status of your work career, athletic accomplishment and family life. Now I understand that these are simply byproducts of success rather than a representation of success. Success isn't the attainment of the results, it is the process of getting there.

Entering this class I thought I had a pretty good handle of what morals are and thought for the most part things were either black or white morally. My view on this could not have changed more over the weeks of this class. It seemed as though every week we were discussing the morality of one topic or another and I would find myself hopping from one side of the argument to the other during these discussions. At first this bothered me because I felt as though I should know right from wrong and I should have an opinion on the morality of these subjects. However I grew to become more comfortable with the ambiguity of certain moral issues and I have come to the conclusion that although in some situations I may feel strongly one way or another it is often not a good decision to try and force my morals onto other people. What is moral for one person may not be moral for another just as I have friends who cannot drink because their religion tells them it is immoral for them to do so. In the end I believe that being a moral person means staying true to your beliefs and values even when the situation dictates that it may be difficult to do so; being a person of strong character who will not stray for personal gain. I think this was an extremely important topic to cover during this class because many of us will work in corporate America and our moral compasses will be tested with very difficult work situations.

I also learned a great deal in this Class about making ethical decisions in terms of what is best for all. For example sustainable economics is a topic that I find very interesting and disappointed that I had never heard this term before, even though I was an economics major in undergrad. It is something that I will carry with me throughout my life along with the importance of treating natural resources as capital instead of income is a concept that I will try my hardest to instill in anyone that will listen.

I feel that I have gained and learned more from this class than any class I have taken at every level of schooling in my entire educational career. I never had a class that made me take such a deep look into myself and discover what was necessary for me to be truly happy. I have learned many life lessons that I will carry with me as long as I live.

Even right now, I am on page three of what is supposed to be a ten page final reflection paper and I am enjoying this moment, enjoying the introspection that this paper is allowing me to go through. Before I had taken this class I would have moaned and groaned my way through completing this assignment but now I feel alive while I type away."

Professor Meyer: "Thank you, I'm humbled and encouraged by your words. Who's next?"

Student: "This Class talked more about issues than any single class I have ever been in during my twenty years of being in school. We discussed topics such as wealth creation, modern society, ethics, social issues, the environment, religion and lifestyles. While all these topics were interesting to me, I will select the topic that had the greatest impact on me, that of personal finance and wealth creation.

The passion I got from this class to understand the power of money could be my most important takeaway from my entire MBA program. I feel very fortunate that I was able to take this Class as I added it at the last second due to a friend's recommendation.

For many years, money had been a mystery to me. I always knew that it was important, but I had never grasped money in the way that I understood it. While I studied and understood money in a business sense from my undergraduate business education, I had never been able to translate that into how it could be incorporated into my life. What this class gave me was the passion and guidance to pursue my quest for financial knowledge. I am now well on my way to understanding money and that is a core life skill that will be with me for many years to come.

My family's perspective on money had a significant impact on the way that I view it. Our household annual income is approximately $165,000. This amount of income puts us in the top ten percent of households in the U.S. The overall actions of my family however tend to lead towards aspiring to wealth as opposed to wealth generation. Two primary factors lead me to this conclusion, their choice of housing and my parent's differing views on finances.

In our textbook '*The Millionaire Next Door*' it stated that the number one determinate of a person's lifestyle and consumption habits was their choice of housing. My parent's particularly my mother, wanted to reach up and buy a nicer larger house in a more prestigious neighborhood. My parent's had the philosophy that they wanted to own the cheapest house in the nicest neighborhood which as our book pointed out ended up being a poor financial decision.

The biggest issue that my parents faced when moving into the new neighborhood was their new social circle of friends. It wasn't long until we became good family friends with many of the people living in this nice neighborhood who were making three to four times more income. All of a sudden, my family felt pressure to keep up with the Jones'. This step up to a nicer neighborhood cost my parents much more than just the price of the new home. The increased amounts of money spent on entertaining, vacations, cars and general living expenses rose tremendously. This caused conflict between my parents.

My mother is the classic example of wealth aspiring. She made the statement many times she has a champagne taste and a beer budget. A perfect example of this can be seen with the purchase of her latest car, a new BMW 335i with a twin turbo engine. Many of my mother's friends with household income several times higher were getting new luxury cars and my mother felt she needed to have one as well. Her car cost approximately Sixty Thousand dollars more than twice what the average millionaire would spend on their vehicle. To add insult to injury, not only could our family not truly afford this car, but she bought a sports car with an upgraded engine when she doesn't ever drive on the freeway or drive faster than forty five miles per hour as she doesn't feel comfortable at faster speeds and is afraid of trucks and merging on/off the freeway.

Other things that classify my mother as wealth aspiring person include frequent eating out, daily dry cleaning visits, multiple vacations each year, excessive personal grooming expenses and entertaining. Her consumption habits are very close to being out of control. Largely because of her overconsumption lifestyle my family carries large credit card debt on a monthly basis. My mother feels that she deserves this lifestyle because she works. The truth of the matter is that if she didn't overspend as much as she does she might not have to work at all. My father has told me that my mother working ends up costing us more money than it brings in.

My father on the other hand has the exact opposite view of money. For example he enjoys home cooking better than going out and spending money. He shops at Wal-Mart researches purchases and is very conservative in his consumption habits.

As you can imagine these two very conflicting ideas about money causes a lot of conflict in my family. This entire issue could have been largely avoided if my parents decided to stay in their original home. This would have changed their social circle, their lifestyle expectations and their normal expenses. As the book stated, and my parents proved, when you move up to a larger home the higher price of the home is just the beginning.

The average household income in the US is approximately $50,000 a year. Upon graduation from my second master's program, the average starting annual salary for the 2008 class was $110,000. The average starting MBA salary for my girlfriend is $90,000. This would make our household income 200,500 per year. This annual income would put us in the top three percent of the US in terms of income according to the US census information, more than four times what the average family makes a year.

While it is easy to get excited about that number, there is also risk associated with it. As seen in the example of my parents, having a higher than average income alone is not enough to become wealthy. It is the decisions that we make with that $200,500 per year that makes the biggest difference.

In our readings, it said that the profession with the highest risk to over consume is the corporate middle manager; a position I will likely be in, because they are constantly striving to reach the senior levels and attempt to imitate the company's executives in their spending habits.

My girlfriend and I have talked about living on half our take-home income. We think it would be very realistic to be able to live on twice the average income in the US and still have a high standard of living. The general ideal is to live below our means and invest the rest. Thank you Professor Meyer, this class has changed my life."

Professor Meyer: "Thank you. Your reflections validate my efforts. Next?"

Student: "The topic in this class that had the most influence on me was meditation and its benefits. I used to think that meditation was only meant to help people become calmer. I discovered that it could help me focus and be in the present. My mentor in the Campus mentorship program used to say we need to enjoy the train ride and not think about the stations. Being aware and present means exactly that, enjoying life. Since this Class, I have started meditating. Now when I talk to people I make sure to not get distracted and focus on what they are saying. Also when I find myself getting stuck in traffic instead of getting angry or annoyed, I just wait patiently and use the time to look around and process the day. It's all about perspective.

In Chapter seven of '*The Compassionate Universe*' it speaks about how love begins when you forget yourself. My relationship with my husband got stronger and more meaningful after I started thinking more about his needs than mine. In return, he puts me first and our relationship is so much richer.

This Class teaches us to be responsible, to protect the individual while keeping in mind the consequences of our individual actions on the community however small or big we chose to define it and to pursue wealth, but the good kind.

I have learned that I can live below my means and that does not mean sacrifice, it means being responsible. And it also allows me to reach my goal of being financially independent. I used to feel the pressure of having to get a high paid, high responsible job that comes with an eighty hour work week, but our discussions in class made me realize that it is more important to go after what I want and am passionate about. That will make me a lot happier and the money will follow. Thank you for a great class that has been a life-changing experience."

Professor Meyer: "You are welcome. And thank you for your contributions to the class during our many discussions. Next?"

Student: " *'Small is Beautiful'* was arguably my favorite textbook of this Course. People today only place a value on that which they create. The (we) do not place enough value, if any, on the environment. Value in the business world has come to ignore nature as something without worth until it is transformed into a product. It is with that mindset that people have lost perspective on what defines them as successful. Instead of recognizing the beauty of the world and our opportunity to appreciate it, people have become caught up in the modern machine of trying to create nothing out of something. People continue to destroy in order to create. And it's not just the environment that is being destroyed it's our identities as people. Misplaced value has steered communities into never feeling satisfied as they try to keep up with the Jones'. Worse, industry has crippled wisdom. According to Schumacher, 'the cultivation and expansion of needs is the antithesis of wisdom.' It is also the antithesis of freedom and peace. Schumacher continues to make this powerful statement, one that will shape the way I hope to manage.

'That should-destroying, meaningless, mechanical, monotonous, moronic work is an insult to human nature which must necessarily and inevitably produce either escapism or aggression, and that no amount of bread and circuses can compensate for the damage done – these facts which are neither denied nor acknowledged but are met with an unbreakable conspiracy of silence – because to deny them would be too obviously absurd and to acknowledge them would condemn the central preoccupation of modern society as a crime against humanity.'

I want to gain success, but I'm not willing to do so at the cost of the environment or my life. I don't want to lead a mechanistic life, nor do I want to be the type of leader who directs those that follow into a life of monotonous activity free of individuality and thought. This, I know will be one of my life's greatest challenges, and this course helped me to realize that.

I once read about the 'Paradox of Success' with essentially means that you could work your entire life and receive great fortune doing so, but when all is said and done, all the money can't buy back the life you gave up trying to achieved what you only thought would bring happiness. This is something all people can potentially fall victim to. If people recognize the value of nature and health, then perhaps they won't feel unaccomplished and defined by what they own.

Ultimately since I can't control other people, I'll start with myself. I will let my values define who I am. As Gandhi said, 'my life is my message.'

Professor Meyer: "Thank you, well said. Next?"

Student: "The most important skill I learned from this classis is to apply critical thinking. We learned how to approach problems how to solve problems that we have not encountered before; we learned to become problem solvers with strong analytical skills and a sharp mind. Critical thinking more importantly includes questioning your own beliefs, questioning what influences our beliefs and why we think a certain way. This kind of critical thinking is not often applied and we certainly do not focus on it during our graduate education. I wish there would be more classes that focus on this kind of discussion and encourage student to question things more. I took too many of my beliefs as set in stone. Partly because I felt that these beliefs were soundly reasoned, well thought through and to a certain degree right. This class has reinforced my way of life and also I have learned a lot of new things. I have broadened my horizon and have improved how I live my life. Through the many open and honest discussions from my classmates about their perspective on so many different issues and to open my mind to things I never thought about before. These made me question why I believed the way I did. I enjoyed that my beliefs were being questioned not because someone was trying to attack me or trying to convince me of his or her opinion, we questioned each other to help each other understand ourselves better. It was certainly a great experience to have something like that in a classroom environment. For me graduate school is not only about acquiring business knowledge, but more importantly about growing who I am. Only by applying this kind of critical thinking will I really have a strong foundation for my life.

I enjoy open communication and when Professor Meyer suggested that we adopt the philosophy 'not to give offense or take offence' but to engage in critical discussion it was inspiring to see what happens when such an environment of trust is created and people can speak their mind and differences of opinion and they are not perceived as attacks on our personal beliefs but rather as a discussion that helps to come to a broader understanding of things. I like to be challenged by others and to have my views and beliefs challenged so I can challenge them myself. I tend to question my beliefs more when others show a difference in opinion and I try to understand what they think and what that says about my point of view. In this respect this class has been an inspiration: I strive to create more in such a trusting environment. I also hope to instill such an environment into my future company where honest and open communication and critical thing are practiced instead of office politics, behind your back talk, and non-genuine behavior. I think this kind of business venture can promise a lot of success because people would actually like to work there and enjoy what they do and therefore be better at what they are doing."

Professor Meyer: "Thank you. The world will be a better place by your efforts. Next."

Student: "In my own life I am more committed than ever to placing morality and ethics in the driver's seat. Don

Johnson, CEO of American Business Bank once told me that it was far more difficult to maintain strong ethical standards in good times than it was in bad times. He cited the example of the housing boom in the mid-2000s. During a time when most banks were growing at unprecedented levels, Don refused to expand ABB's core business in order to artificially capitalize on this inflated growth. Even after the board of directors challenged Don to reconsider his decision he maintained a firm ethical insistence on conservatism. This strong moral compass made Don's life more challenging during the good years, but as soon as the housing bubble burst and banks of all sizes began to fail, his fortitude began to pay off. Due to Don's high ethical standards for his company, firms started to move their accounts to ABB as quickly as the paperwork could be completed. Too often moral relativism is used as a guise for skirting inconvenient ethical standards. But for those who hold true to values they will always be able to sleep at night. One of my favorite movie lines noted that "What we leave behind is not as important as how we've lived."

Professor Meyer: "Thank you. Well said. Who's next?"

Student: "Two of the most influential things I have learned in this Course are about simplicity and meditation. The concept of simplicity reminds me of the Spanish word *aprovecha*. This Spanish word is interesting because there is no exact English equivalent for it. There is no direct English translation for 'spending just enough' or living in harmony or balance through one's spending. This fact alone is an indication of how we Americans feel about this subject, how the simplicity of *aprovecha* is not important enough that a word be dedicated to it in our language. In *Your Money or Your Life* we learned that *aprovecha* means to use something wisely, to get a certain value from something in a way where you are getting all of what something has to offer and living in the moment as you do it.

As Americans our commitment and obsession with business, whether it be our own venture or working for a corporation has sucked up so much of our precious resources that most of us don't even have the time to go home and reflect on what we're doing and what we're missing out on. So how does one find simplicity in our complex, overscheduled and business oriented lifestyle? The answer is to integrate simplicity into our daily lives and take time out to find simplicity. Integrating simplicity would not be quitting our jobs, but find a way to ride a bicycle to work, by being outside we would be more connected to nature and take pleasure in the simple act of seeing and interacting with the environment around us in a closer way. Integrating simplicity could mean having dinner with our families and not sending text messages or watching television in the background and focusing on the basic interactions we have with one another. We must make adjustments that make simplicity a priority.

Having guests over for dinner at my house was a more complicated ordeal than necessary because my mother was obsessed with putting on a spectacle that would show the guests how much effort had been put into the meal, which would serve as a sign of how much respect and appreciation we had for them. But she had lost sight of simplicity. As much as our guests loved the great food they were more interested in our company, in the jokes my dad told, in hearing about the lives of myself and my sister and enjoying the simple conversation more than the elaborate meal. Food and drink are merely complements to the real focus which is the simple interactions that we have with each other."

Professor Meyer: "Thank you. Those are valuable observations. Who's wants to go next?"

Student: "Eknath Easwaran's book The Compassionate Universe has taught me a lot through this Course. I've enjoyed reading about his perspective on life and seeing ways in which I can change my own life. Easwaran focuses on an environmental application to life in the modern world where various external factors play a vital role in our personal life and wellbeing. He states 'Because we still believe happiness lies in remaking the world around us, we look for inner fulfillment outside ourselves and this makes us easy prey for manipulation.' (Easwaran p. 41) I think this statement really relates to my own life in that I'm constantly looking outside myself for satisfaction, happiness and fulfillment. I constantly worry about what other people think, look for acknowledgement and approval, and focus on others rather than focusing on my inner being. Easwaran has taught me to look inward to find peace and fulfillment in life. This has been a very crucial lesson for me because I feel that I'm at a place in my life where I'm finally figuring out what I want to do and deciding the next big steps to make.

I also learned from Easwaran's further emphasis on the world as a whole that I am individually responsible to respect Mother Nature and live in harmony with everything around us. I've tried to practice this social responsibility throughout my life, but Easwaran has brought me further emphasis on where small things add up to make a difference. I loved his small example of bringing a cup with him when he goes to a place like Starbucks to send a message of preservation for the earth. I've stared to do the same and found some places even give you a discount for bringing your own cup.

I found Schumacher's ideas of how modern day economics should work in comparison to how they are actually working very fascinating. I had never really thought about economics from that viewpoint and was surprised at how much sense it made. By being socially conscious of the economic decisions we make we can take into account various aspects that we otherwise might not. I think it is important to consider the consequences of every decision we make and assess who and what it will affect in the long run.

I always thought I was a free thinker, but I've learn through this Course that there are so many things that influence my thinking. My conservative family has had a big influence on the way I think. This class has really helped me to develop my critical thinking and given me a broader range of opinions and experiences. I really appreciated the viewpoints of student who are from different countries other than the U.S. It was wonderful to learn about their different cultures in contrast to ours. I especially enjoyed their perspective on American culture and hear the differences as it related to business, wealth, spending and ethics.

Living a life that is in parallel with my beliefs and goals is my personal definition of success. I want to continue to move toward the true north of my moral compass and make sure that everything I do is something I can be proud of."

Professor Meyer: "Thank you for your contributions to the class. I think they will be beneficial to all who come in contact with you going forward. Next up."

Student: "In my mind I split this Class up into two categories. On one side we had the money management education and on the other side we had the spiritual education. How those two worlds mix and mingle was perhaps the most valuable and intriguing part of this Course.

Before this Class, I would never have connected the two but now I have a new view of what money does, but more importantly I have a new understanding of what work really is. The biggest benefit I got out of this Class was to help me to visualize how I see myself accumulating wealth in the future and the way I want to go about working to accumulate this wealth. The two biggest challenges people have in life center on how we are going to spend our time and what environment we are going to choose to put ourselves in to make money AND the other is how we as individuals relate to the rest of the world and universe. These two issues are interesting because besides money and wealth they are things that people think about all the time. How we relate to the world is among most people's primary spiritual concerns.

The Book '*Small is Beautiful*' struck a chord with me since it talks about the beauty and viability of small businesses as opposed to large businesses. Schumacher makes many good points and successfully sets up the case for why smaller business is better for the universe and the world than big business and I tend to agree with him on most points. This was somewhat a difficult topic to explore since in business school we are groomed to work for large corporations and taught processes that are pertinent to the large corporate world. This Class went against the notion to some degree and taught that small is better and more responsible than big. These books pointed out examples of how big corporations don't act responsibly. For example, larger corporations tend to market products without considering the consequences that these products might have on people and the environment where a smaller company has the ability to realize the impact that marketing of a product might have on the consumer. I had a problem with this because in school we're taught to grow companies. This is the goal of any business; see how big you can get. When in actuality this is not the best scenario for everybody. Consciousness does have a place in commerce. One must make decisions within the context of how that decision affects others and the environment and align with the values of your customers and those around you."

Professor Meyer: "Thank you. It's encouraging to hear a business student think about such things. Who's next?"

Student: "The idea of meditation had never occurred to me. Like most I had preconceived notions about what meditation was. I thought it was some sort of religion or ancient philosophy that had little use for my job or personal journey. When the guest speaker came in to talk about meditation I was open minded and didn't know what to expect. Can this stuff actually be practical? The principals of meditation were introduced and how this is not considered religious but more of a rejuvenating experience that can clear your mind. I said to myself, maybe this can be useful after all. I guess the phrase that struck with me the best was that meditation clears the mind of the racing thoughts we have in life. Now this can really help me in my personal journey and in my current job. Meditation brings things to a singular state clearing racing thoughts from taking hold. For me, I have trouble being worrisome. Always thinking about the future with thoughts like what will I do in the future, what type of job will I have. In essence through meditation I learned this is not living in the now. The thought of now really means now. It means one. Enjoying and embracing the present. To many times I have racing thoughts that are hard to shake off. Practicing meditation with our guest speaker was an interesting experience. Going through the process after closing my eyes I was trying to focus on the breathing entering and exiting the exact point on my nose. I was trying to fixate this image in my head and have the rest of the world fall from my thoughts. At first it was tough. Thoughts like what did I just hear, tended to come to the front of my mind. As we eased into the practice it became a little easier and midway through the exercise I was in the zone. As we got closer to the end I broke out of my concentration and had my mind wander about other things. As a whole the experience was great. The question and answer period with the guest speaker was very informative. She explained about the practice as a whole and how meditation is always a work in progress. Nobody has ever mastered it and the same troubles the class was having were the same troubles others had that have been practicing meditation for decades. In addition when Professor Meyer spoke about the application of meditation from a personal experience it was encouraging. That he like our guest speaker had not missed a day of meditation for over twenty five years speaks volumes of how if something in your life is so important you will go to no end of believing in it. This shows how will-power can be a very powerful and setting your mind to something is more than half the battle.

Professor Meyer: "Thank you. I hope you too can someday say that you have not missed a day of meditation in many years. Next."

Student: "The topic in this Course that most influenced my thinking was about the idea of 'consequences'. I liked how the idea that everything is not good or bad just everything comes with the prospective of consequences. I liked how the Course set the framework of life as a set of consequences. I liked the idea that Professor Meyer set out a catch all thought process that if a decision would not lead to a peaceful sleep that it was not something he would do. I haven't had someone explain things like that to me and it was very insightful and added a great thought balance for me."

Professor Meyer: "Thank you for sharing that. Next."

Student: "The topic of this Couse that influenced me the most was thinking critically about the idea of how to live frugally. Frugality is often perceived as cheap, but in the Course distinct differences were made. The general perspective I came to see was to live below your means. For everyone, below your means has a different context. Americans in particular have gained an excessive amount of debt in life due to the fact that they live above their means. It is driven into everyone's life at an early age from either their families or from the media that why would you want to live frugally? This course was a good illustration to show me that even though I might not make a huge salary saving money is possible. The discussions about breaking down daily spending habits were very interesting. For example the Class exercise about not spending any money for a day was interesting. I planned ahead for the week in having all my necessities met. My car's tank was filled with gas, food stocked for all my meals and snacks brought with me to work and class. I took all the cash out of my wallet and was not tempted to spend any money. This trained me not to depend on money throughout the day. Sometimes money is used as an escape from something that you can overcome without money. Often I use money in a situation that is not needed to be spent especially with food items. When I am out of my house I find myself spending money uselessly on snacks and food that if I planned ahead of time would not drain my bank account. Again and again frugality has many dimensions another being that choices on purchasing items need to be examined. It was described that you do not have to never buy something but use the resources around you to work for you. This class was a good awareness that saving money is not a hard thing to do but something that can be broken down in parts of your life.

With living below your means I learned about the idea of not having your personal items own you. Like others I am engrained to get the newest product that often turns out to run your life. The example of this is the IPod like we discussed in Class is a great picture of an item that people spend large amounts of money on that blocks them from the outer world and learning about nature. By questioning these thoughts that everybody seems to be doing in this world I know I am on the right track.

Moreover, the trap of the media and the questioning about where we came up with that from was influential. From the talks about Valentine's Day to 'once in a lifetime' opportunity experiences ideas that have been taught in this class that challenged the foundation of society's acceptance. We are all too often victims of the media.

Additionally, the part of the Course that added perspective was the comparison between the United States society and the international students' perspective. There was a great blend of international students like from Cypress and Morocco from Germany and Togo from China and India who added differing ideas. In most classes we only look at the American view when solving a problem and do not take other countries or societies in consideration. For example some of the German students explained that there were no homeless people in Germany. The government and society eliminates homelessness which from an American viewpoint is quite opposite. These were great eye opening conversations that shows sometimes the American way is not always the best."

Professor Meyer: "Thank you for that perspective. Who's next?"

Student: "The part of this Course that influenced me the most was on how we can break habits. That is not about breaking them overnight, but the concept of breaking things down one day at a time. Instead of thinking of something as impossible to overcome, breaking it down into simple ways. For example I am trying to eat healthier. Instead of planning out saying 'I am going to do this for one month', instead saying 'I am going to do this for the next meal.' This was a great application for me."

Professor Meyer: "Thank you. I hope you continue to challenge your habits. Next?"

Student: "I liked the tempo of this class, lecture, discussions, guest speakers, power points that were short. These added great value to the Course. Often in classes the professors put on a slideshow for four hours and lose the attention of the students. This class wasn't about punching out spreadsheets or making sure numbers were correct. It challenged me to think critically and challenged my preconceived notions on critical issues in life. Some of the topics were not normally what we talk about in other Classes.

With the aid of great speakers and a diverse background of students the topics of this Course were great. My personal exploration through the Course was an engaging ongoing process. It broke down the thought process I was taught in life and left me with some of my old ideas mixed with some new perspectives. What I took away was not to change my view, just challenge my views. Challenging things I took for granted in life and don't fall trap to some things in life that some do."

Professor Meyer: "Thank you for sharing that. Who's next?"

Student: "In Class, when asked if any of us would work for a cigarette manufacturer I said I would do so. While this might be a difficult choice because cigarettes are known to kill people, I also need to be wary of what is important to me, which is my family. I justified the decision to take such a job under the condition that it would pay well and provide excellent benefits and ultimately allow me to provide for my family. My decision was in part because I believe that someone else is going to do the job and that these tobacco companies will continue to make cigarettes with or without me. However, in taking such a job I also believe there could be an opportunity to try and promote change from within. While this may be self-serving as a means to make me feel better about the hypothetical career I chose, it also serves the purpose of my own wealth and pleasure. Soon after I declared my position similar comparisons were brought up, such as working for a company that manufactured missiles and bullets. Since that class, I know that my response would be different now. The class discussions and our reading have reshaped my perceptions. I have since realized that making the choice to work for the tobacco company while serving my family's wellbeing would be pursuing my own pleasure at a cost to others. When weighing this out I ultimately realized that I would be unhappy doing so and become further aware that I cannot compromise my morals for the sake of wealth no matter what propaganda guides me towards. My transformation came as a result of what proved to be one of the most interesting aspects about this discussion – the varying opinions. Hearing so many points of view and the differing reasons as to why or why not one would take such a job exhibited the array of critical and analytical thinking of my fellow classmates. I was able to filter through the opinions and take out certain points that I had never considered and readjust my own opinion.

In addition to many of the other lessons I learned in this Class the assignment we were given to discuss our desires proved to be incredibly eye opening to me. One's desires especially for instant gratification can often be blinding to long term happiness. I have never paid much attention to the origin behind the desires that fill my life and consume my existence, but rather just accepted those desires were things I actually needed for happiness. I never asked myself questions. One of the most prevailing questions I had never considered asking before this Class was 'why do I/we work?' I just assumed that I worked so that I could earn a paycheck or make a living. I believe that the end means was to have the capability to purchase food, shelter and clothing. But to also fulfill my desire to have things that I wanted rather than needed. I want certain things so that my family will be comfortable and happy like a nice house in a good neighborhood, for example. I also want things to make me feel relaxed, comfortable and happy. The question this exercise brings up however is 'Why do I desire such things?' In the past I had never examined my need to fulfill these desires, but this exercise enlightened me as to the origin of most of my desires.

When I was in secondary school my classmates and I became much more affected by entertainment and advertisements that were thrust upon us from all angles. Though I was clueless at the time, I know now that my peers as well as I were strongly affected by these messages and images. Coupled with the teenage desire to find one's social niche this became an overwhelmingly powerful connection. Whenever one of my friends or myself would get something new there was the usual feeling of happiness, but there was also a tinge of hidden jealousy. This one-upmanship led to deeply rooted desires that in my case would prove to be a significant motivator in my life's decisions. For example, I look at my friends who are well along in their careers and I cannot help but to compare myself to them, wishing I had their success while I am instead trying to figure out my own career. Through this exercise I have been able to recognize this problem and perhaps establish the framework to reduce or even eliminate my unnecessary desires. As Professor Meyer said the Buddha identified desire as 'the cause of suffering.' So hopefully by becoming aware and eventually reducing my desires my self-awareness will increase and thus reduce any suffering.

This is where critical thinking comes in and why this Class's focus on the development and the use of our ability to think critically has been so beneficial to my journey over these past weeks. The emphasis of critical thinking has led me to ask more questions, both of myself and of others. It is no longer acceptable to just take someone's opinion as fact. There are almost always two sides to whatever the topic is being discussed. The ability to listen to others can be extremely valuable, yet is often underutilized. Listening to others viewpoints can serve multiple purposes. First it creates an atmosphere of trust and allows the other person to know that you care about what is being said. Second, by listening attentively and not just focusing on your own next thought it allows you to fully absorb what the other person is saying thus making your response all the more informed and relevant.

Listening to others is also important in the way we make decisions and choices. Before going forward with a decision it is to one's benefit to hear both sides of an issue. As a result of this Class I now recognize the importance of hearing both sides fully and equally before coming to a decision.

This idea was complemented by Professor Meyer when he asked us to consider the idea that most decisions programed into us are done so by people who benefit from that point of view. He asked us to consider who that decision benefits and who does it hurt. Also whether the decision takes us closer to our goal or further away from it.

Perhaps the most important lesson I will take from this Class is one that I wish to employ for the rest of my life. That of 'full effort means full reward without worrying about the end result.' In the year or so leading up to my first day of business school and perhaps going back even further in my life, I have been a victim of anxiety. This anxiety is the result of my need to be good at the things I do. However, rather than wholly commit to any action I often make preemptive excuses so that I am not let down if the outcome is not what I hoped for or expected. The philosophies discussed in this Class from Buddha to Gandhi to Lao Tzu to Melville have ignited a deeper understanding and confidence in my capabilities. If I fail, then that is okay. Failure is life's way of presenting us with the opportunity to learn. As Professor Meyer said in quoting inventor Thomas Edison 'I have not failed, I succeeded in finding 10,000 ways that won't work.' It is time that I take responsibility for my actions and be proud of the work I produce as long as I know that I have put forth my best effort.

Professor Meyer: "Thank you for sharing that. Good insights we all need to keep in mind. Who wants to go next?"

Student: "Before this Class, I did not believe one person could make a difference in the world. I consider myself to be a realist and I think most things through logically. I know that one person boycotting a company that employs child labor will not cause that company to file bankruptcy. One person taking a three-minute showers every day and reducing their energy usage will not save enough resources to help the planet. Ironically, it was our class discussion about diamonds that made me re-evaluate my beliefs. As we learned, it took De Beers many years to build the reputation and status that diamonds hold. But now, as many students mentioned, the idea that a woman cannot get married without a diamond ring is spreading to other countries. When I heard this, I figured that if a manipulative act or idea can spread so easily, the same should be true for an altruistic or beneficial act.

I used to get discouraged from taking action because I thought my positive actions would mean nothing when compared to other people's negative ones. However the knowledge I gained in this class made me realize that other people's actions should not influence my own. I hold no power over what other people do or say, I can only exercise control over myself. Professor Meyer said that if you want to change the world you have to start by changing yourself. I no longer feel discouraged from taking action, no matter how small. Because if everyone keeps thinking the way I used to think, there will never be any change in the world. However, if more people made small changes, there would inevitably be an impact. It is our responsibility to make choices that not only help ourselves, but others and the world around us. Allowing myself to be led by desires is a selfish act. I can only help those around me by stepping out of a self-centered mode and making wise and prudent decisions.

Asking myself why I hold my values or where I get certain philosophies from was the most challenging aspect of this Course. Professor Meyer asked us why we wanted to get married or have children. At first I was not sure if these were something I sincerely wanted to experience or if I was programmed to desire them by society. Was I just playing follow the leader and allowing someone else to make my decisions for me? Did I really want to settle down with one person for the rest of my life or was I just following societal expectations? People rarely ask themselves such difficult and probing questions. I remember a couple of students in class having issues with their values and the jobs they wanted to have. One of these students wanted to practice marketing once she graduated from business school, but at the same time, she did not want to manipulate people into buying items they did not need. I have the same qualms about business practice, because many aspects of business are not about helping others and society as a whole, instead the bottom line in business is increasing profit.

My current professional goal is to find a way to combine my personal values of helping people and giving back to society with a career that I enjoy and pays me well. I do not want to engage in any activity that robs me of peace and tranquility in my heart and mind.

I greatly appreciate the opportunity to examine my values and opinions. I consider my life too valuable and precious to waste it following someone else's guidelines or rules. Now that I have critically analyzed my viewpoints on various ethical and societal topics I feel that they have been strengthened. I know I have the freedom and the ability to make my own choices. By incorporating the steps of mantra, meditation, detachment, frugality and the concept of critical thinking into my life I will be able to live life on my own terms. The power to choose my own way will give me control over how I want my life to turn out."

Professor Meyer: "Thank you for sharing that. Who's next?"

Student: "I think one of my favorite things Professor Meyer talked about was worry. I just keep retelling his words to my friends because I think they are so valuable. I have been using prayer/meditation to deal with this issue and it is working effectively. I also try to remember him telling us 'worry is like running your car engine without going anywhere; It wastes time and it drains the energy.' This is so true. A pastor once told me 'Sometimes I feel like things are getting out of hand, but then I realize they were never in my hands.' This is also true. If I cannot control it I am not going to worry about it and if I can control it then I am going to do something about it; either fix it or cut my losses.

I really liked when Professor Meyer talked about worry and thoughts being like a movie film. He said something along the lines of 'when our thoughts go by so fast they are like a movie that seems so real, but when we slow them down we can see there is really no connection between the frames they are separated by space and we can find peace in that space between the frames.'

I pray a great deal. I have become more methodical about prayer in the past year and a half. I find that prayer is not something we are compelled to do every day. We get tired sometimes, we are in bad moods, but we do it anyway, like exercise. When I give my worries and thoughts over to God, my world is a better place. I can find the silence in my mind that Professor Meyer talked about. I am more connected with myself. I am more able to care for myself and more able to give to and love others. I really liked our

guest speaker who took us through the exercise on meditation. It was so valuable. I think however without Professor
Meyer priming the meditation concept I would not have
been open to him. However he was very world-religion oriented. There was nothing about his spirit that sought to
bend mine to his ways. The entire class increased my open-
ness allowing my beliefs to be complimentary with those in
meditation.

The day he came, someone hit my car right before class.
After meditating purposefully in the middle of the day I
found so much value, clarity, awareness, joy, peace and focus
from the meditation. I have words to say to God and then I
let my mind go blank for periods of three to five minutes. I
can refocus my mind just by saying Jesus. I am going to start
praying for longer periods with more silence of word and
thought in my mind. I realize the value tenfold now.

People with integrity act in accordance with the values they profess. 'Let us live, not in word or speech, but in
truth and action' 1 John 3:18. Values are only ideas until
they are realized into action or as Gandhi said 'My life is
my message.' I value, faith, orality, fortitude, compassion
and self-control. The virtues I prize and seek to display are
the fruits of the spirit, these virtues I value above all else.
Integrity and character are defined in the moments that we
walk through fire and we come out the other side as more
pure substance, all the impurities are burned away and we
are left with our core values, strengthened and polished by
trial and tribulation.

This Class has taught me to use critical thinking as to
why I believe what I believe and where the genesis of my

beliefs came from. I have always questioned but not to the degree or depth or ways in which this Class has challenged me. Plato discusses that prisoners set free from the darkness of the cave would become frightened, but his Class helped to ease me into not becoming frightened to seeing things in a different light. My mind, body and should have been set free, I choose freedom of thought rather than compulsion of need. I have been unshackled and for this I am thankful."

Professor Meyer: "And I am thankful to you for sharing that. Who wants to go next?"

Student: "Seven weeks went by extremely quickly, yet I feel that I am a different person already. It's amazing how much change can take place in such a short amount of time.

One challenge this Class has offered me is to question society's norm. For example frugality has a bad reputation, but I kept asking myself why? Current economics tells us that consumption is good because it increases profits, which increases business expansion, which increases jobs and which further increases consumption. However this denies that the world has finite resources. Increased consumption has the added effects of pollution, genetic defects in both human and animals and other adverse consequences. It has been proven time and time again that consumptions does not bring happiness. There seems to be an inverse relationship as living below your means allows less debt, less stress and more time. Knowing this we are still being taught in most classes that consumption is necessary and good. The media perpetuates this by showing celebrities with luxuries and makes the assumption that they are happy. What it doesn't show is that a great deal of the affluent are actually frugal and happier than celebrities.

The meditation also had the effect of limiting my emotional urges and compulsory habits. Instead of just giving into these I was able to shift my attention away from them and understand where they came from and why and what thoughts were surrounding them. I feel that meditation has proven to be a very effective tool for helping me question my beliefs and bring more awareness in various areas of my life.

A difficult challenge throughout the Class involved questioning my own beliefs. I saw the contradictions when Professor Meyer said 'Your beliefs are as deep as your actions.' For example I believe that animals are treated poorly and there needs to be changes made in this area yet I continue to eat meat and support companies that depend on animal cruelty. I believe that pollution is a problem in order to provide decent living environment for future generations however I drive just as much and continue to pollute; my actions contradict my stated beliefs. This Class has brought these contradictions to the forefront and introduced the idea that the only way the world can change is for me to change. The more I cling to my beliefs the more limited my awareness. I did not hold this same view when I started the Class. Only after discussions did my perspective begin to change. For example I always assumed that polygamy is illegal for good reasons. However, when questioning this belief I did not find any reason why it shouldn't be legal. In another discussion about free market versus government involvement I first held to my belief that the government can and should come in to solve issues most of the time. But as more students addressed the implications of this, the more I questioned my beliefs and I concluded that I really did not know the answer. These thoughts about beliefs are a work in process and I will continue to think about them much more in the future and my beliefs will likely change. One thing for certain I have realized that the values and beliefs I have are often in contradiction with my actions and I hope to make changes that will align them.

Another great challenge of this Course was in the first day when Professor Meyer asked me 'if money was not an issue what would you do with your life?' I said I did not have an answer and that was partly why I enrolled in this Course. While I still do not have a specific answer I understand that this is fine because I have the tools and knowledge to guide me in the direction of finding happiness of doing something that aligns with my values. I want to be someone who understands when enough is enough. I want actions to reflect my values and life purpose. I want to ask not what I can get, but what I can give. These are all changes and goals for me and this fits with one of the conclusions of this Course that the best way to change the world is to change myself. In the spirit of this final paper I am pleased to announce that when class is over in April I am planning to apply as a volunteer with the Peace Corp. While I will be helping others I will also meet new and interesting people with similar concerns for our world and environment and have the added benefit of discover myself further. This may lead to some more awareness and perhaps I will finally be able to answer the question of what I would do if I didn't have to work or go to school. I am excited."

Professor Meyer: "Thank you. I'm excited for you too. Please keep in touch and let me know how the Peace Corp experience has changed your life. Who's next?"

Student: "As valuable as this Course has been to my personal and financial awareness and growth and development as an individual over the past seven weeks the path has not been an easy one. I have been given the tools necessary to take an unbiased critical look at my lifestyle, spending habits, goals, desires and conviction and have been challenged to reassess and reevaluate my belief and standards in each and every one of these areas.

The first topic I would like to discuss is the same which we started the class with on the very first day. If I never had to worry about money again what would I do with my time? Would I still be on the same career path I am on today? I suppose I am fortunate in that I am one of the few students who would continue working in the same industry regardless of financial dependence on the job. I have been working part-time as a board member for a non-profit foundation for the last five years, a position which I plan to pursue full-time upon graduation. Even if I never had to work again I would still find something productive to do with my time as I am the type of person who needs something to work towards in order to find meaning in my life. I need to be able to apply myself to something greater than my own life in order to feel I have a purpose. Similar to what Victor Frankl wrote in his book *Man's Search for Meaning* 'A man who becomes conscious of the responsibility he bears toward a human being who affectionately waits for him, or to an unfinished work, will never be able to throw his away his life. He knows the 'why' for his existence and will be able to bear almost any 'how.' I have found that whenever I start to lose meaning in my life and whenever my problems start to feel like the weight of the world on my shoulders, all I need to do is volunteer somewhere or involve myself in bettering the life of someone else and suddenly my problems don't seem too bad. Similar to the journal exercise on mantra focusing my attention on someone else takes the focus off my own issues and give me the time and ability to reassess my situation and how I am choosing to react to it.

Two very accomplished people I have met gave up their high status, ultra-high paying careers with companies that did not represent their values. They chose happiness over their jobs and salaries, a difficult decision at the time, but one that proved to be worthwhile in the end. One of them recommended to me that I try my hardest to find a job that I enjoy as there is nothing worse than getting up every day with a sense of dread and despair. There will always be some aspects of work that I do not like, but overall I must enjoy it. Any legal job is a respectable job so I should not be ashamed of whatever path I choose. He also warned me that I should not get to comfortable with an organization that I do not like or else I may feel stuck and unable to change my focus once I have others who depend on my income like family and children. Money is important, but attaining some meaning of fulfillment is more important. More often than not it seems as though people take jobs they hate in exchange for higher pay and for these types of people the work life balance does not seem to exist. While I am not in the position to say what works best for anyone other than myself I do know I want a career that I wake up in the mornings excited for the day and don't want a career that slowly sucks the life out of me. I want to achieve a balance between work and life and reap the rewards now, rather than live a miserable life and reap the rewards in forty years because who is to say that I will still be alive or physically able to enjoy it then.

In all this class has given me the ability to document my goals in life and the tools I need to achieve the life and lifestyle that I not only want, but need as well.

Something that I have fought against most all of my life was simple living but thanks to this class it is beginning to make more and more sense. I live in a fire prone area and my friend has had her home burn down three times destroying everything she has accumulated in her life yet she remains an incredibly positive and happy individual whom I have an immense amount of respect and admiration for. I was not fully able to understand how all this interplayed in my life until Professor Meyer made the simple statement that after basic comforts have been met, the more we have the more that it takes away from life. We no longer own it, but rather it begins to own us. This statement hit me like a hammer to the head and something stirred inside of me that really resonated with it. So much of my life and my time are consumed by material goods and it is not something that always gives me pleasure. As much as I receive enjoyment from some of my items, there is an equal amount of time if not more in which they cause concern; concern over theft, over fire or natural disaster, of damage to the goods, paying for them etc. Then there is the time spent on maintenance and the time spent on searching for more. It sounds so superficial and pointless when I look at it as such, though perhaps this is why I have had such a stir in this class. The discussion we had on detachment has given me the tools I need to detach myself from these goods and achieve the wisdom in how to deal with materialism. I also hope that achieving detachment will ultimately help me to conquer desire as well. I have had such amazing revelations come to me from this Course, but the result of which is the realization that I have a steep uphill battle ahead to achieve them.

In summary, here are some of the notes I have taken in class along with descriptions of how I intend to use my learning to become wiser, more in charge of my fulfillment in life.

Relationships:

a.   If I go in thinking things will be 50/50 I will never be content. If I go in thinking they will be 70/30, it will probably be more like 50/50 and I will likely still not find peace. Rather I need to go in 100%.

Morality:

a.   Nothing in life is worth disrupting my peaceful sleep (peace of mind)

Critical Thinking:

a.   'Your belief is a deep as your action'

Philosophy of Happiness:

a.   WE all have an assumption of 'happiness' and 'the good life'. Many times these assumptions are not fully conscious and are untested assumptions.
b.   When we think about money we think about things that it allows us to do. Money is not the highest good, but it is looking at what we think will really make us happy.

Goal/Achieve/ Detachment

a.   Without detachment we can never have wisdom.
b.   We must detach ourselves from desire and choose our actions. Selfishly oriented desires cause suffering because not all our desires can be met.
c.   The best things in life and those that make us the most happy are those which we do by choice rather than compulsion.
d.   It is the love of money not money itself that is the root of all evil.

Meditation:

a.   Meditation is a tool which can help single out thoughts and can help achieve detachment. A tool to retrain our habits.

b. It is one way to see moment by moment what causes happiness and what cause stress.

c. About becoming more functional in the lives we lead; how we use our attention in the lives we live.

d. Can raise the baseline level of clarity, less foggy, more aware, increase awareness, improves concentration, ability to what is relevant. When the mind is gathered everything is a little more fulfilling.

e. Can help in the ability to give you things that compound stress.

Pleasure vs. Joy:

a. Pleasure is short term enjoyment; Joy is long term inner peace.

b. Long-term success and happiness, vs. short term satisfaction.

c. We have been programmed to want immediate satisfaction, yet you gain so much more by saying no to instant gratification. We need to reprogram ourselves to start making our own decisions.

Simple living:

a. More doesn't equal better.

b. The simpler your life, the happier you'll be.

c. After basic comforts have been met, the more we have, the more that stuff takes away from life. Possession start to own you; example public storage.

d. Environmentalism: A simplified life is the best way to be an environmentalist for the more we consume the more we damage the environment.

e. Great idea: Don't buy groceries and see how long I can last living off of what I have in my cupboard and refrigerator; also helps one avoid the temptations of the supermarket.

f. Before buying anything, stop and ask myself, 'Do I really need this? How much will I get out of it?'

Frugality equals smart spending, not cheapness

a. Frugality is the key to wealth.

b. There is no shame in using coupons.

True Cost of a dollar

a. After tax cost is not the same as cost.

b. Something that costs ten dollars is an after tax cost of ten dollars which means it probably took me twenty dollars of my time to accumulate enough funds to pay for it.

c. Once I received my first paycheck I was able to experience firsthand what I had heard my parents talking about all those years and what I had been told to expect throughout my years in school and through studying politics: The government takes away forty percent of my paycheck.

d. Develop a way of thinking why am I buying this. Is this really worth the money it costs. Need a strong understanding of what the value of things are to me.

Formula for Spending and Saving:

a. I have plans to have fifty percent of my paycheck automatically go into a savings account. The remaining fifty percent will be used first to pay for the necessities such as property taxes utilities etc.
b. Understanding my spending in particular my unconscious spending is incredibly effective as a means to help me bring my spending under control.
c. Money is not ours to spend, to become wealthy we need to save. Just because I did not spend money on something does not mean I have that money to spend on something else. Instead I take that money and save it, putting it in another bank account then forgetting about it is an excellent method to help me save.
d. One day a week I have chosen not only to not spend anything, but to take what I would have spent and invest it instead.
e. Ultimately, develop an awareness of what I do each day and what I spend money on.
f. Remember even the small things add up. Need to avoid thinking 'It's only ___. Because all of those 'it's only' adds up.

Pain in the Break

a. It is difficult to acknowledge my weakness, but in order to mend the wound sometimes we need pain in the break to reset things in a position so that they can heal properly.

Closing Remarks:

I would like to make a few remarks about the last seven weeks and how far I have come despite such a short period of time having passed. This class has taught me to take a step back from my life and try to assess what is really truly important. Through meditation, reflection, self-analysis and continued education through books, discussions, critical thinking, I feel optimistic that I have the ability to break the bad habits in my life, and the ability to control my actions. Although I know it must sound like an exaggeration, this class has encouraged critical thinking more than any other class I have ever been enrolled in and it has been the most stimulating, most practical and one of the best taught classes I have taken in my entire life. I am a bit frustrated to know that most of this may come across as simple flattery, but I feel so strongly about the course and what I have learned from it that I am willing to take that risk. Not only can I apply what I have learned here to my business career, but it is highly relevant to my personal life as well.

This is honestly what I had hoped Grand Reflection University would incorporate into more of their classes, relevant knowledge, critical thinking, moral and ethical issues, money management, financial insight and an overall amazing professor. It is classes like this that I have been yearning for throughout my educational career. We can truly get in depth on a subject and explore not only what we think, but why we think and hold certain beliefs which is the essence of critical thinking. I have clung tightly to so many different beliefs in my life that I claim to be so passionate about yet I was shocked to find that some of my seemingly core beliefs have little to no backing; I am responsible for the same thing I have critiqued others for; having opinions with no reasons or knowledge behind them. I have learned more about financial health, wealth management and financial planning in this course than any fiancé or typical business class. Other classes taught me how to read an income statement, but this class taught me how to use my income to create wealth, stability and ensure a successful future.

When I first read Victor Frankl's book '*Man's Search for Meaning*' the message truly resonated with me that I cannot control anything else in my life other than how I respond to the situations life presents to me. I cannot control those around me I cannot control my environment and I cannot always control my circumstances. However I do have the power over how I react and respond to those situations, however horrible and seemingly hopeless they may be. When we are no longer able to change a situation, we are challenged to change ourselves. Between stimulus and response, there is a space and in that space lies our freedom and power to choose our response. In our response lies our growth and freedom. Everything can be taken from a man, but the right to choose one's attitude in any given set of circumstances; to choose one's own way."

Professor Meyer: "Thank you for those very insightful reflections. Unfortunately we have run out of time. I assure those of you who did not have an opportunity to present that I will read every word of your Final Reflection Papers. With the few minutes we have left I would like to leave you with these thoughts.

Well known author and alternative medicine advocate Deepak Chopra in his course for MBA students at Columbia University says he views capitalism as a vehicle for doing good. He then goes on to say, 'I define spirituality as self-awareness and also as elements of compassion, love, service, honesty, authenticity and integrity. I think even if you don't relate to those values, if you incorporate those values your business is going to thrive. By setting daily intensions and practicing meditation, you can evolve your leadership skills in business and life. I set the intention every day for a joyful energetic body, loving compassionate heart, reflective alert mind and lightness of being. And then I don't worry about anything, the rest of the day organizes itself around those intentions.'

E.F. Schumacher author *of Small Is Beautiful; Economics as if People Mattered* says that universal prosperity is possible because as Gandhi said, there is enough for everyone's needs but not for everyone's greed. Then goes on to say, 'you can disarm greed and envy by being less greedy and envious yourself. By resisting the temptation of letting our luxuries become needs; and perhaps by scrutinizing our needs to see if they cannot be simplified and reduced. By stop valuing over the top consumption and mega wealth. Stop considering consumption to be the sole end and purpose of all economic activity and work to put our own inner house in order.'

Note too that this same advice is found in your text *The Millionaire Next Door*, where the authors say to stop measuring our standard of living by the amount of consumption, to consume less and look at clothes, cars etc. as utilitarian and not status. And to look for quality and value in terms of the service it is intended to provide; a car should last for 20 years, clothes for many years etc.

The inner strength to transform ourselves says Schumacher, can be found in a quote from Gandhi, "there must be recognition of the existence of the soul apart from the body.' Stop considering goods as more important than people.

Schumacher also suggests that for the system to work, 'workers must have meaningful work and not be exploited as robots.' This same observation can be found in Huxley's essay on the industrial revolution where meaning for life is lost in robotic like work.

Schumacher and others offer, there must be a respect for nature. Respect for wisdom over intellect and wisdom over cleverness. To do this you must first liberate yourselves from such matters as greed and envy. Wisdom can be read about but it can only be found inside oneself. Be still and know that I am God. Stillness produces the insights of wisdom which are obtainable in no other way. And it enables us to see the hollowness and fundamental unsatisfactioness of a life devoted primarily to the pursuit of material ends, to the neglect of the spiritual.

The difference between intellectual knowledge and wisdom is that intelligence involves how you gain knowledge and skills, and your ability to interact with the world around you, but wisdom is about more than just having knowledge – it pulls in one's judgment and experience too. With spiritual wisdom you will always know what to do. Intelligence is typically associated with innate and unchanging ability or IQ. While wisdom refers to the qualities of having experience, knowledge, and good judgment.

Wisdom can give you an edge or the ability to handle information appropriately. It helps you directly affect outcomes. Practicing it showcases your best self. You build relationships where you're not only safe to be yourself, you allow and encourage others to do the same. Think of wisdom as the proverbial magic wand that boosts the quality of your life.

Wisdom also includes the willingness to embrace and learn from differences. It includes the power of compassion and understanding. When you show these to others, they're less likely to feel threatened by you, more likely to open up and be honest with you, and more willing to share their ideas with you. Co-operative solutions come from this safe place.

Wisdom gives you the ability to handle information appropriately. Using your wisdom while exercising discretion allows you to do many things including:

- Figure out what's necessary or best to share
- Speak up now or later
- Back down permanently, until a later time, or until circumstances change
- Stay silent
- Take a certain course of action

Acquiring wisdom is not simple or automatic. It's a lifelong process which includes making your own mistakes and learning from them as well as seeking wisdom from those you respect.

Wisdom is knowing that data is important, but that it is not the only thing that should be used to inform your decisions. It's realizing that people, relationships, and giving back matter and should always be considered in all of your decisions and interactions too.

Wisdom is about pulling in from the totality of areas that you have at your disposal – your networks, expertise, skills, experience, and emotional intelligence while strict intelligence is more limited and fixed.

Wisdom involves learning from the things we've failed at in addition to those we've been successful at and having the confidence to realize that failing is central to our growth and should always be seen that way and embraced.

Wisdom is learning through trial and error, seeing the value in everything and everyone and embracing feedback from others including people and perspectives that are different from our own.

Knowledge is the acquisition of information; wisdom is knowing and having the experience as to how to use that information.

Intelligence is understanding the 'how'. Intelligence is digging past the superficial and getting to know the truth concerning a subject, principle, or object — how it functions or works. Wisdom is understanding the 'why'.

We have been acculturated to accept truth as paramount, but wisdom is knowing how to apply the truth, when to discard it or even reverse it, because you understand the deeper why — the deeper concept or essence.

As you go forth on your life's journey remember the wisdom in this Zen parable of the Tiger and the Strawberries that illustrates how to live in the present. It's about a monk who is being chased by two tigers. When he comes to the edge of a cliff, he looks back and the tigers are almost upon him. Noticing a vine leading over the cliff, he quickly crawls over the edge and begins to let himself down the vine. When he checks below he sees the two tigers waiting for him at the bottom of the cliff. When he looks up he observes two mice gnawing away at the vine. Just then he sees a beautiful strawberry within arm's reach. He picks it and enjoys the best tasting strawberry in his whole life! Although only minutes from death, the monk enjoys the here and now. Our life continually sends us tigers and it continually sends us strawberries. But do we let ourselves enjoy the strawberries? Or do we use our valuable consciousness worrying about the tigers? Note that the monk fully responded to the physical danger in the most intelligent way. He ran from the tigers and he even scrambled down the cliff while hanging onto a vine. And having done this, he remained fully in the here and now to enjoy whatever life offered him. Doing everything he could do, he used his precious consciousness to fully enjoy every moment of his life. For all of us death is a part of our future, but we do not have to become what the existentialists refer to as the living dead. We can always find things to threaten us or we can consciously perform whatever action is needed and then turn our attention to enjoying everything we have to enjoy. We always have enough to be happy if we are enjoying what we do have and not worrying about what we don't have.

Thank you for the honor of being your professor, for being open and curious about life and for sharing your inner feelings, your visions and your passions. I have two gifts for each of you, a copy of Eknath Easwaran's book entitled *Your Life Is Your Message* so that you might consult it daily to start your day in an affirmative direction. And a laminated book mark I have inscribed with a few reminders from the

Course such as, *spend less; practice your mantra and meditation daily* and; *how to determine the right thing to do by asking yourself the following questions, Who will benefit from my decision? Who will be harmed by it? Will I gain a short term benefit at the expense of a long term one?*

Now go out into the world on your journey with confidence and compassion and if you have a mind to, keep in touch, I would love to hear from you. Class dismissed.

The End Is Prelude

Acquiring Wealth, Power, Success, Morally and Ethically (AWPSME)

COURSE TEXT BOOKS

The Millionaire Next Door, by Thomas J. Stanley, Ph.D and William D. Danko, Ph.D

Stop Acting Rich: And Start Living Like A Real Millionaire, by Thomas J. Stanley, Ph.D.

Your Money or Your Life: 9 Steps to Transforming Your Relationship with Money and Achieving Financial Independence, by Vicki Robin and Joe Dominguez.

Small Is Beautiful, Economics as if People Mattered, by E.F. Schumacher

Ethics in Motion, by Justin M. Paperny

The Compassionate Universe, by Eknath Easwaran

RECOMMENDED READING

How to Give Your Kids $1Million Each, (And It Won't Cost You A Cent), by Ashley Ormond

Meditation, by Eknath Easwaran

The Mantram Handbook, by Eknath Easwaran

Taming Your Mind, by Ken Keyes, Jr.

A Conscious Person's Guide to Relationships, by Ken Keyes, Jr.

The Scandalous Gospel of Jesus, by Peter J. Gomes

Life's Operating Manual, by Tom Shadyac

The Documentary "*I Am*", directed by Tom Shadyac

The Bhagavad Gita For Daily Living (three volumes), by Eknath Easwaran

EPILOGUE

"Professor Meyer, I'm so happy to find you on Facebook! I was one of your students in my MBA program in 2015. You were the best professor I ever had and I have carried your words of advice with me since I left that school. Thank you, thank you, thank you for making a difference in my life. During the hardest parts of it, your words have given me courage and kept me strong. I wish you so many blessings and good fortune and I hope you're very happy in every part of your life!"

"Hello Professor. I don't expect you to remember me, but just wanted to state that after almost ten years since graduating from GRU, your classes were one of the most important and educational I have ever had the privilege of completing. Hope all is well with you Sir."

"Dear Professor Meyer. Thank you so much for your class I took many years ago, Acquiring Wealth, Power, Success Morally and Ethically. Eight years later I have paid off more than $185,000 in student loan debt, am now 100% debt free and have increased my net worth by more than one million dollars since then. The Course built foundations and opened the door to personal finance for me. Thank you so much! PS: I celebrated this millstone with a brand new Jaguar paid for in cash!"

"Professor Meyer, It has been almost six years since I received my MBA. I wanted you to know that you where the most positive influence in my life. You are a great teacher and your Class AWPSME was awesome, the best I had at GRU. Great readings, great discussions, critical thinking. It was real graduate work!!!"

"Professor Meyer, I found you on LinkedIn. Your teaching have meant a lot to me personally and in my career. You are one of the best, most intelligent teachers I ever had the privilege to learn from. I hope you are well."

"Dear Professor Meyer, I want to thank you for your class AWPSME, it was the Perfect Class the kind that GSU should be like! I'm still using my mantra every day and meditating too and they have changed me in every way for the better."

"Professor Meyer, just a note to let you were a great mentor to me and I think of you often. Your class was pivotal in my life and career. I liked the critical thinking and moral and ethics. The open discussions. Great teachings and great lessons learned. Great readings. You are one of the best teachers GRU has ever had."

"Professor Meyer before I left GRU I told the Dean that your class should be a required Course. Other classes do not mention how to align values with work. Your Course was unique. It overlaps with other MBA courses providing a completely different perspective that is very practical and applicable to all our lives. Thank you for all that you have done to help me achieve a meaningful life."

"Professor Meyer, thank you for a great class. Yours are the only text books I kept and I still read them. Please promote this class to future students so they are aware and can have the opportunity to enroll. Thank you for offering this course."

"Professor Meyer. I want you to know how much I enjoyed your class. The discussions were really great. Just having an open dialogue in a graduate level course was truly refreshing and should be encouraged and promoted in more courses. It really helped me learn more effectively. In addition I got to learn about more people and other's opinions about the subject matter. It was one of the best Courses that I have ever taken at any level of education. Thank you for a great class. I've never had a class that had so much focus on each and every student."

"Professor Meyer, I want you to know that AWPSME was the BEST class of my MBA program. It should be a required class because it falls in line with what GRU stands for and what differentiates its program from other programs."

"Professor Meyer, you have been the most inspirational teachers I ever had and your class easily one of the best I have ever had. Thank you for a life changing experience."

"Professor Meyer. I hope you get this message. I want you to know how much your Class has meant to me. It was the best one of my MBA program. It was engaging and forced critical thinking, and the guest speakers and short videos presented during class were relevant and educational. The course books were AMAZING. I will be keeping them for years and years to come and I have bought the list of recommended reading items as well. Thank you. I wish more professors put these types of lists out. Class assignments were relevant and encouraged students to seek the advice and input from other students. I could go on and on. Excellent course, taught by an incredible man. If it was at all possible for me to re-take this course, I would jump at the chance. I hope more students learn about this Course and I only wish I had, had the opportunity to have lecture and discussions like this in my other classes. Thank you again. I hope you are well."

"Professor Meyer. I want you to know that your entire course was extremely effective. The variation of textbook subject matter allowed us to see different perspective. The open discussion was also a great way to learn and explore in the classroom. The objective was to enhance critical thinking. Your Course should definitely be required for every student. Also the guest speakers' were a contribution to the class. I use what I learned every day in making decisions in my business and personal life. "Does this decision take me closer to my goal or further away from it? "What are the consequences?" "Is it true? Is it necessary? Is it kind?" Thank you for a great class."

"Professor Meyer, I would love to come and see you. You were my favorite Professor at GRU and I learned a lot from your wisdom. The one story that I remember most was about the Monk and the Strawberry and I recount it often on difficult days. Why lose the now for the future? Also in our conversations we agreed on much but also vehemently disagreed on some and you never let that affect your attitude in any way. Best Regards."

Made in the USA
Monee, IL
19 September 2023

43021987R00223